Aspects of Applied Geography

DEVELOPMENT & HEALTH

Morven Archer
(Principal Teacher of Geography, Annan Academy)

Series editor: Martin Duddin
(Assistant Rector, Knox Academy, Haddington)

Hodder & Stoughton
LONDON   SYDNEY   AUCKLAND   TORONTO

ACKNOWLEDGEMENTS

CONTENTS

The author and publishers thank the following for permission to reproduce photographs and material in this book. Robert Harding (cover); A M Warnes 1.1; Mark Edwards /Still Pictures 1.4, 1.5, 1.9, 4.3, 4.14; Compix 1.8; WaterAid 4.11; Sally and Richard Greenhill 4.15.

Every effort has been made to contact the holders of copyright material but if any have been inadvertently overlooked, the publisher will be pleased to make the necessary alterations at the first opportunity.

British Library Cataloguing in Publication Data

Archer, Morven
Development and health - (Aspects of applied geography)
I Title II Series
362.109172

ISBN 0 340 55395 2
First published 1991
© 1991 Morven Archer

Printed in Great Britain for the educational publishing division of Hodder & Stoughton Ltd., Mill Road, Dunton Green, Sevenoaks, Kent by Thomson Litho Ltd., East Kilbride.

1 WHAT DO WE MEAN BY DEVELOPMENT?

KEY CONCEPTS

Location, Spatial pattern, Diversity

Figure 1.4

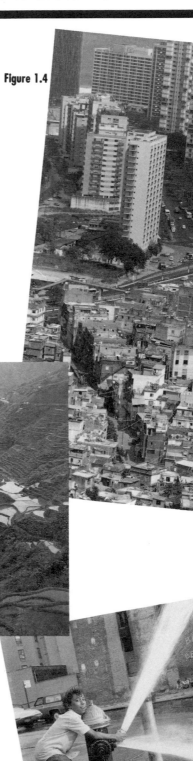

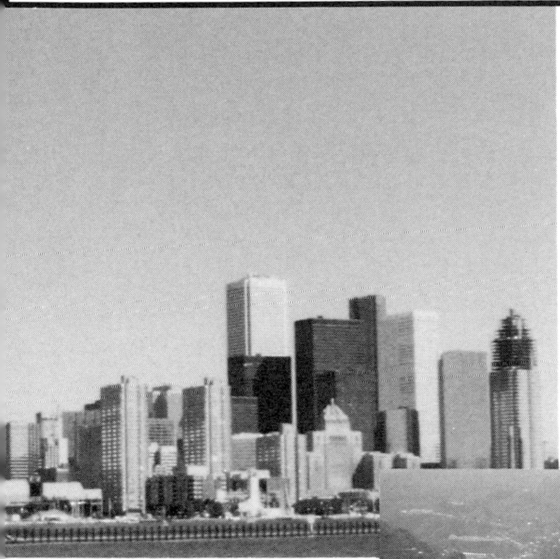

Figure 1.1

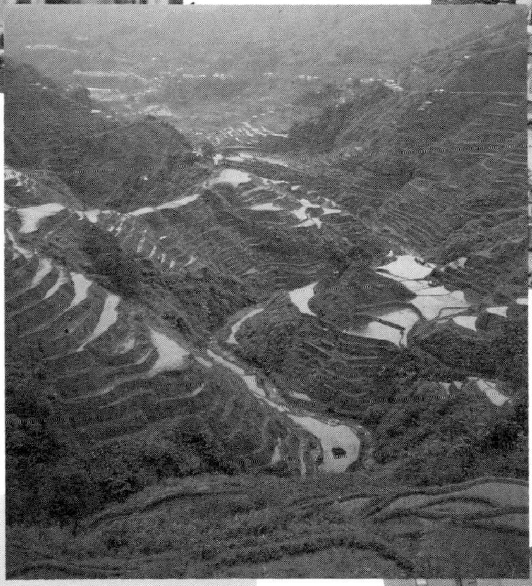

Figure 1.2

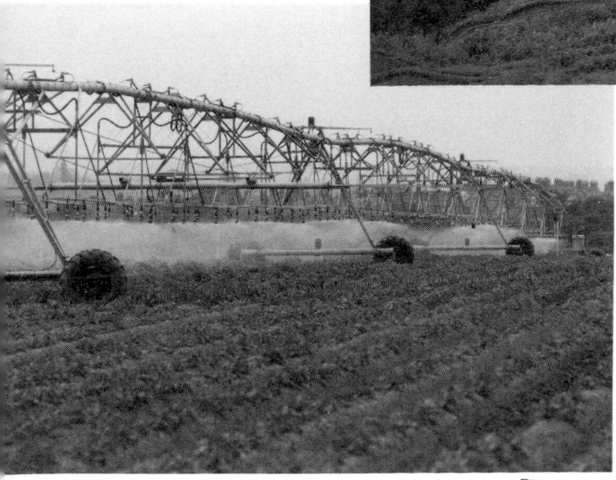

Figure 1.3

Figure 1.5

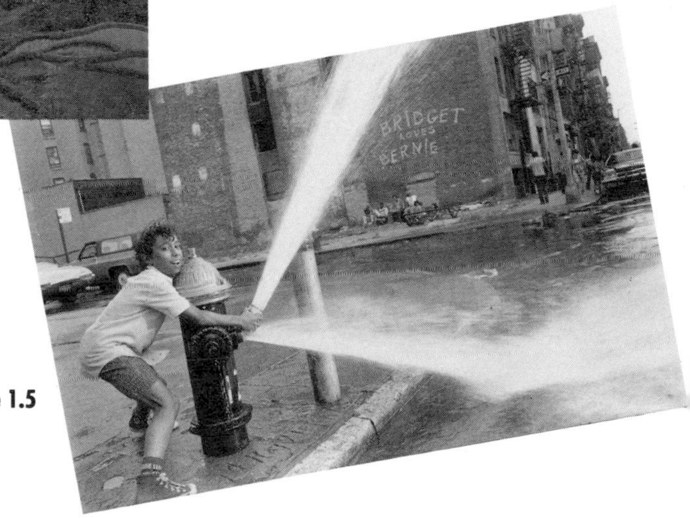

1 Look at figures 1.1 to 1.5 and the photograph on the front cover. For each decide if it is typical of the Third World or the Developed World.

2 Give reasons for your decision.

Many of you will have made your choices on the level of wealth apparent in the photographs. (The actual locations of the photographs are given at the bottom of page 40.)

Development Indicators

One way of measuring levels of development is to look at how wealthy or how poor a country is. To do this, GDP (Gross Domestic Product, ie the total value of all the goods and services produced in a country) and the GDP per capita (GDP divided by the total population) can be measured. The figures for GDP and GDP per capita are average figures for the whole country. These are usually called **Economic Indicators of Development.**

3 Look at table 1a.
   a) Which countries would you consider to be Developed?
   b) Which countries would you consider to be Less Developed?

Country	Population ('000s)	GDP (m$)	GDP/capita($)
A	246 330	4 497 220	18 448
B	57 080	575 740	10 120
C	14 020	71 470	52 518
D	8 920	1 960	225
E	24 000	3 080	133
F	144 430	299 230	2 115

Table 1a

4 Can you suggest one problem of using GDP per capita when discussing an individual's wealth within a country?

In the past, using economic indicators such as GDP was considered to be the best method of measuring the level of development within a country. Today there is less certainty about this as it has been clear that high growth rates are possible in the Third World which have had little effect on the standard of living of the majority of the population. Other methods of measuring development have to be studied.

Another method of measuring levels of development is to look at the quality of life on offer to people within a country. There are a great variety of indicators which can be used to measure this, eg life expectancy, infant mortality, number of people per doctor, birth and death rates per 1000 (these all help to measure the quality of medical services available) and literacy rates (this indicates the availability of education to the population). These are called **Social Indicators of Development**.

PHYSICAL QUALITY OF LIFE INDEX

Three indicators - life expectancy, infant mortality and adult literacy rates - are considered to be especially valuable and can be combined to produce a measure called the **Physical Quality of Life Index** (PQLI). For each of the indicators the worst figure is allocated 0 and the best 100 and each figure in between is scaled to a figure between 0 and 100. The average of these three figures for each country is then calculated. Seventy seven is regarded as a satisfactory level, below this the quality of life is poor (see figure 1.6). Table 1b shows the same six countries as those in table 1a, this time showing three of the important social indicators. You will see that it highlights some interesting differences.

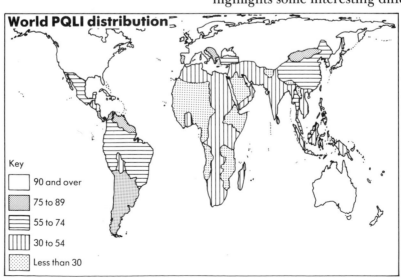

World PQLI distribution

Key
90 and over
75 to 89
55 to 74
30 to 54
Less than 30

Figure 1.6

4

Country	Life expectancy	% Adult literacy	Infant mortality/ '000
A	76	99	10
B	75	99	9
C	64	16	69
D	47	7	168
E	53	66	104
F	65	78	61

Table 1b

Use table 1b to answer the following questions:
5   Which two countries would still be classed as being part of the Developed World?
6   Which country is now not part of the Developed World according to these figures?
7   Which country, classed as part of the Third World, has high adult literacy rates?

You may also notice that country F, which did not fit too easily into either the Third World or the Developed World category, according to GDP, is again somewhere in between.

PQLI INDEX				
Country	Life expectancy	% Adult literacy	Infant mortality/ '000	PQLI
A	76 (98)	99 (98)	10 (97)	98
B	75 (95)	99 (98)	9 (96)	97
C	64 (51)	16 (12)	69 (61)	41
D	47 (29)	7 (5)	168 (31)	22
E	53 (41)	66 (65)	104 (56)	54
F	65 (77)	78 (75)	61 (68)	73

Table 1c

Use table 1c to answer the following questions:
8   In which two countries is the quality of life high?
9   In which two countries is the quality of life low?
10   Which country has almost achieved a good quality of life?

The three sets of figures show how dangerous it is to rely on a limited range of indicators when looking at a country's level of development. It is probably always best to have a mixture of economic and social indicators, **Composite Indicators of Development.**

Why were there differences between the countries? This is best explained by revealing the identities of the countries: A = USA; B = UK; C = Saudi Arabia; D = Mali; E = Tanzania; F = Brazil. The USA and the UK are rich countries, part of the Developed World and are easy to classify. Mali and Tanzania are part of the Third World. The high literacy rates in Tanzania are due to the Tanzanian government's campaign to provide elementary education for all. Saudi Arabia's oil wealth is concentrated in the hands of a small number of people and the government has not developed social welfare programmes for the majority. Brazil is a country which is beginning to move from Third to Developed World status as its economy expands.

There are other reasons why defining and measuring development can be difficult; for example, statistics may be unobtainable. Until recently for instance, it has been very difficult to obtain statistics from communist countries. Statistics from Third World countries may often be unreliable. Also it is difficult to measure quantitatively aspects such as freedom of speech and minority rights, which differ widely in different countries. Even in countries which are classed as Developed there may be certain aspects in which they are nearer to Less Developed status.

Who's Who?

There is a maze of terminology used to describe the state of a country's development:
Developed/Developing
First World (Western industrial nations)
Second World (communist economies)
Third World (the rest)
Rich World/Poor World
North (the First and Second World countries)
South (the rest)
LDC (Least Developed Country)
MDC (More Developed Country).

The term North/South first appeared in the Brandt Report in 1980. The term LDC was first used in 1968 by the UN Conference on Trade and Development in an attempt to focus attention on those countries with severe problems and to try to promote help for them from the wealthier nations.

Look at figure 1.7.
11   Why is the term North/South confusing?
12   What do you notice about the location of the majority of the LDCs?
13   Compare the location of the LDCs with countries which have a low PQLI as shown in figure 1.6. You should emphasize any discrepancies and attempt to explain these discrepancies.
14   Look at table 1d showing statistics for the 36 LDCs and six Developed Countries and complete a copy of table 1e to show the contrasts between the two.
15   The two photographs (figures 1.8 and 1.9) are both taken in Bangladesh. How do they illustrate the dangers of using average figures when looking at the state of development within a country?

THE 36 LDCS								
Country	1	2	3	4	5	6	7	8
Afghanistan	111	39	42	0.56	183	14	69	0.10
Bangladesh	172	33	52	2.74	119	8	46	0.06
Benin	365	26	47	2.86	110	6	44	0.05
Bhutan	176	n/a	49	2.03	128	4	51	n/a
Botswana	1300	71	59	3.46	67	48	4	n/a
Burkino Faso	199	13	48	2.40	139	11	47	0.03
Burundi	230	34	50	2.67	114	10	51	0.02
Cape Verde	158	47	62	1.94	63	n/a	n/a	0.04
Central African Republic	374	41	46	2.28	132	10	41	0.03
Chad	186	25	46	2.28	132	17	41	0.02
Comoros	198	n/a	52	3.05	80	n/a	n/a	0.04
Djibouti	387	n/a	54	3.60	n/a	8	4	0.28
Equatorial Guinea	220	37	46	2.15	127	1	60	0.10
Ethiopia	104	55	42	2.46	149	10	40	0.02
Gambia	236	25	37	1.94	164	7	28	0.11
Guinea	369	26	43	2.33	147	22	40	0.08
Guinea-Bissau	146	32	46	1.91	132	n/a	n/a	0.04
Haiti	414	38	54	2.51	117	17	32	0.05
Laos	185	84	49	2.23	110	n/a	n/a	0.03
Lesotho	270	73	57	2.53	100	11	16	n/a
Malawi	148	41	48	3.09	150	13	37	0.04
Maldives	393	n/a	47	2.90	n/a	5	51	n/a
Mali	225	18	45	2.81	169	7	53	0.02
Nepal	144	26	52	2.33	128	5	54	0.03
Niger	333	14	45	2.82	135	5	43	0.05
PDR of Yemen	98	42	52	2.76	120	27	19	0.17
Rwanda	321	47	49	3.31	122	17	40	0.03
Samoa	343	n/a	65	0.80	n/a	7	50	0.35
São Tome and Principe	306	n/a	65	2.70	n/a	5	48	n/a
Sierra Leone	234	29	42	1.70	169	17	44	0.07
Somalia	274	12	46	2.93	149	6	41	0.10
Sudan	355	23	51	2.86	106	17	33	0.07
Togo	391	41	54	2.95	93	6	40	0.06
Uganda	214	57	52	3.33	103	6	73	0.03
Tanzania	133	78	54	3.52	106	4	53	0.04
Yemen	584	15	52	2.76	120	14	29	0.70

Six Developed Countries

Country	1	2	3	4	5	6	7	8
UK	10 120	99	75	0.30	9	25	2	5.36
USA	18 448	99	76	0.88	10	21	2	9.49
Sweden	16 930	99	77	0.40	6	21	3	4.89
Japan	19 464	99	78	0.40	5	29	3	3.36
Germany (West)	18 723	98	75	0.00	8	32	2	5.67
Australia	11 337	98	76	1.40	9	22	4	6.74

1 GDP/capita ($)
2 % Adult literacy
3 Life expectancy
4 Population growth per annum
5 Infant mortality /'000
6 Mining and manufacturing as % of GDP
7 Farming as % of GDP
8 Energy consumption/capita
n/a Not available

Table 1d

The Less Developed Countries and the North/South divide

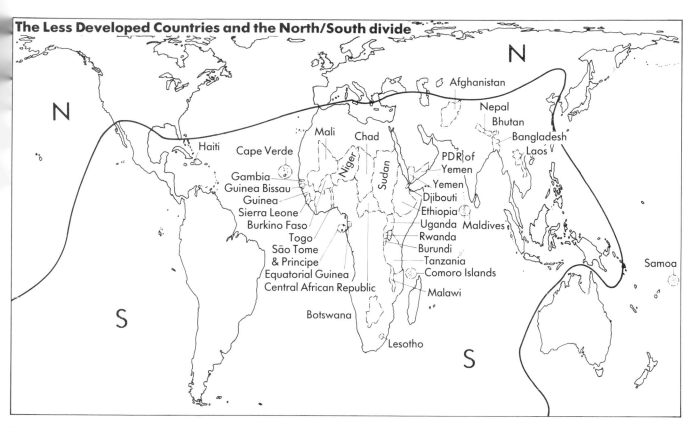

N

N

N

Afghanistan
Nepal
Bhutan
Bangladesh
Laos

Haiti
Cape Verde
Gambia
Guinea Bissau
Guinea
Sierra Leone
Burkino Faso
Togo
São Tome
& Principe
Equatorial Guinea
Central African Republic

Mali
Chad
Niger
Sudan

PDR of
Yemen
Yemen
Djibouti
Ethiopia
Uganda
Rwanda
Burundi
Tanzania
Comoro Islands
Malawi

Maldives

Samoa

Botswana

Lesotho

S

S

Figure 1.7

Figure 1.9 Bangladesh village

Figure 1.8 Dacca

	DEVELOPED WORLD	LDC
GDP		
Types of jobs		
Population growth		
Life expectancy		
Health care		
Education		
Energy consumption		

Table 1e

Case Study: Brazil - Regional Inequalities

The Facts

Brazil is the fifth largest country by size in the world, has the sixth largest population in the world (140 million), has half the land area of South America, and half the population of South America.

- Population density 14.5 per km^2
- Population growth 1970-80 2.48%
- Urban population 63.5%
- People employed in agriculture 19.9%
- Population literate 60.3%
- 10% of the population receive 50% of the total income.

(1988 figures)

REGIONAL CONTRASTS IN BRAZIL

	NE	SE
Life expectancy	48	63
Infant mortality	19	7
Households with clean water (%)	20	78
Households with sewage disposal (%)	25	73
10 - 14 year-olds in full education (%)	57	83

Table 1f

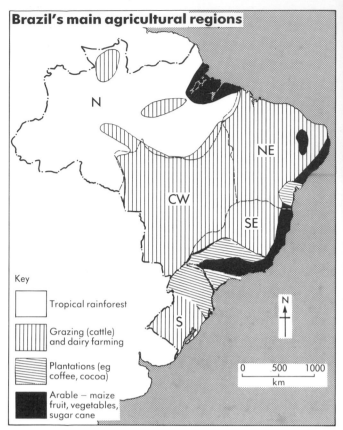

Brazil's main agricultural regions

Key
- Tropical rainforest
- Grazing (cattle) and dairy farming
- Plantations (eg coffee, cocoa)
- Arable — maize fruit, vegetables, sugar cane

0 500 1000 km

Figure 1.11

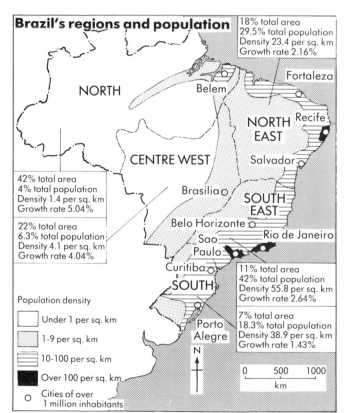

Brazil's regions and population

18% total area
29.5% total population
Density 23.4 per sq. km
Growth rate 2.16%

42% total area
4% total population
Density 1.4 per sq. km
Growth rate 5.04%

22% total area
6.3% total population
Density 4.1 per sq. km
Growth rate 4.04%

11% total area
42% total population
Density 55.8 per sq. km
Growth rate 2.64%

7% total area
18.3% total population
Density 38.9 per sq. km
Growth rate 1.43%

Population density
- Under 1 per sq. km
- 1-9 per sq. km
- 10-100 per sq. km
- Over 100 per sq. km
- Cities of over 1 million inhabitants

0 500 1000 km

Figure 1.10

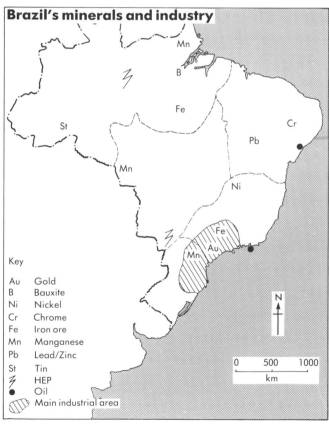

Brazil's minerals and industry

Key
Au	Gold
B	Bauxite
Ni	Nickel
Cr	Chrome
Fe	Iron ore
Mn	Manganese
Pb	Lead/Zinc
St	Tin
⚡	HEP
●	Oil

Main industrial area

0 500 1000 km

Figure 1.12

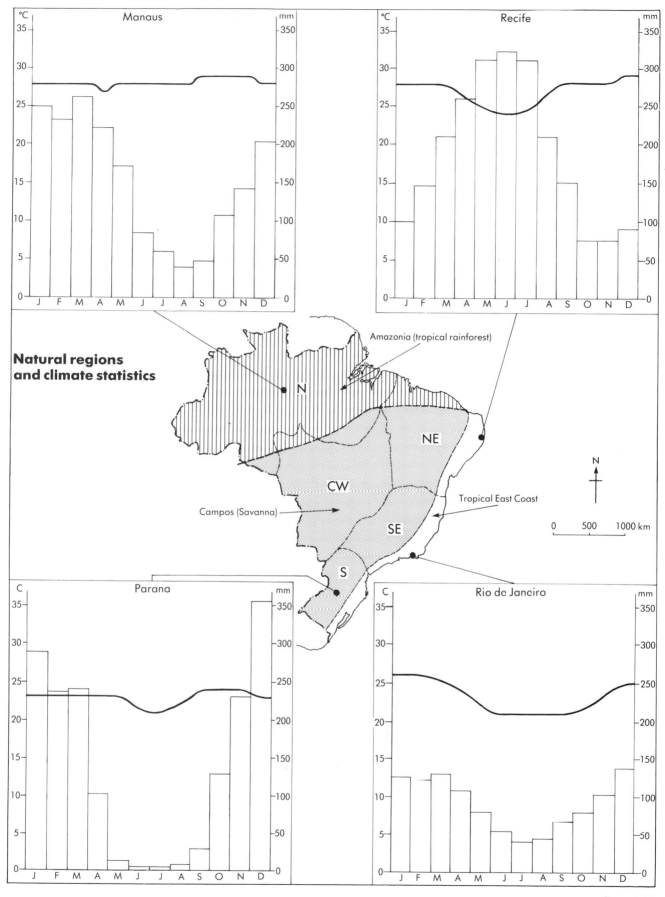

Natural regions and climate statistics

Manaus

Recife

Parana

Rio de Janeiro

Amazonia (tropical rainforest)

N

NE

CW

SE

S

Campos (Savanna)

Tropical East Coast

N

0   500   1000 km

Figure 1.13

9

BRAZIL'S DEVELOPMENT PLANS		
Date	Aims	Problems
1957 - 61	Promote industrialization	No agricultural policy and no social programme
1963 - 64	Maintain the growth rates of 1957-61 Control inflation Reduce regional income inequalities Improve scientific and technological education Reform various institutions, eg banks	Lack of agricultural policy No social programme for health and education No mention of increasing employment No mention of import - export growth rates Did not control inflation Did not reduce regional inequalities
1965 - 66	Improve economic growth rate Combat inflation Correct the balance of payments situation Increase employment Reduce regional and individual inequalities	No good social development programme No mention import-export growth rates Few jobs created Regional and individual inequalities remained
1968 - 70	Increase rate of economic growth rate	No mention of regional and individual inequalities No mention of import growth rate
1971 - 72	Establish country as a developed nation Decrease rate of inflation Stabilize the balance of payments Increase employment Gradual correction of regional and individual inequalities Redistribute personal income Land reform Reform of administration	Lack of social development programme No real reduction in regional and individual inequalities Only gradual progress in other areas
1973 - 74	Have Brazil accepted as a developed nation Decrease rate of inflation Reduce regional income inequalities	Very little mention of agriculture
1975 - 79	Maintain and increase economic growth Correct inflation Maintain stable balance of payments Improve regional and personal distribution of income Improve social and political conditions Develop without lowering quality of life Gradually increase the importance of agriculture	Inflation not mentioned Little mention of social development Employment did not grow sufficiently No population policies
1980 - 85	Reduce regional and individual inequalities Improve income distribution Improve standard of living for all Have equal access to social facilities for all Encourage and improve agriculture Reduce urban growth Control inflation	No direct mention of population policy

Table 1g

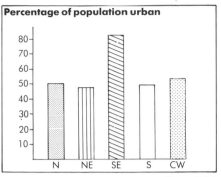

Percentage of population urban

Figure 1.14

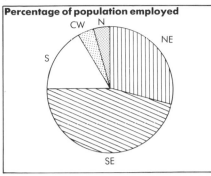

Percentage of population employed

Figure 1.15

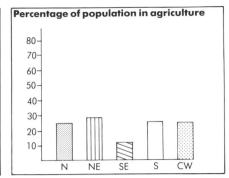

Percentage of population in agriculture

Figure 1.16

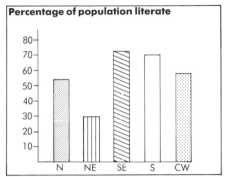

Percentage of population literate

Figure 1.17

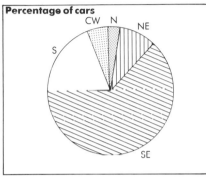

Percentage of cars

Figure 1.18

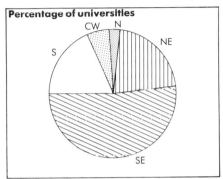

Percentage of universities

Figure 1.19

Sources: NatWest Bank
   Brazil Geofile No 35
   Geography of Brazil Brazilian Embassy
   Anuario Estatico do Brazil

Figure 1.20

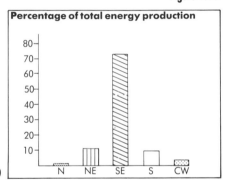

Percentage of total energy production

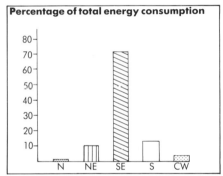

Percentage of total energy consumption

Figure 1.21

16 Why is it unwise to rely on average figures when studying a country's development?
17 Which of Brazil's regions is:
   a) the least developed
   b) the most developed?
18 For each of the regions chosen give reasons for the level of development.
19 What seem to have been the main weaknesses in Brazil's development plans?

Assignments

A Using all the information which has been supplied on the six countries at the beginning of the chapter, write an essay describing their levels of development as shown by the statistics and explain the dangers of relying on a limited range of indicators.

B Use the information supplied to write a report on the inequalities of Brazil's regional development.

SUMMARY

- It is possible to define levels of development by using various indicators, eg economic (measures the wealth of the country), social, PQLI (measures the quality of life).

- It is best not to rely on a limited range of indicators as these can give a false impression of a country's level of development.

- There are many definitions and terms to describe a country's level of development, none totally satisfactory.

- Average indicators for a country do not show up variations in individual wealth or regional variations.

2 MEASURING THE POPULATION

Population statistics on birth and death rates, infant mortality and life expectancy are major social indicators. They are also important when studying the structure of a population, in order to identify significant trends. Using such statistics to draw graphs is also a valuable way in which the development status of a country can be presented and easily compared. Such statistics are also of considerable value to governments as they can be used as part of the planning process in the allocation of finite financial resources. Unfortunately in many cases the figures are extremely inaccurate due mainly to the problems encountered in gathering the information.

Gathering Information

Generally speaking this is achieved by taking a regular census of the population. In the United Kingdom, for example, this occurs every 10 years, with a sample census conducted in the intervening years to check the figures. Such an exercise is a massive undertaking, even for a developed country such as the United Kingdom. Many of the poorer countries of the world face considerable problems in trying to conduct a census of their people.

Read the information on Peru and study Peru in your atlas.

1 Describe in detail the problems faced by census collectors in a poorer country such as Peru. (NB there may be other problems not referred to; check other sources available to determine if this is so.)

2 Why are accurate figures so valuable? (Refer to health, education, housing and social services requirements and industrial development.)

Case Study: Peru

The Facts
- High birth rate - population increase 2.6% per annum
- Life expectancy 61
- Infant mortality 88 per 1000
- GNP $1000 per head
- Malnutrition 30% of population malnourished
- Population literate 80%.

(1988 figures)

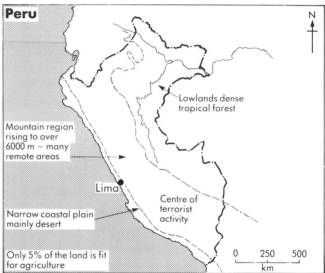

Figure 2.1

Population

The minority - descendants of European settlers, own most of the land, they have the greatest share of national wealth, political power, and good access to medical facilities.

The majority - native Indians, campesinos and poor subsistence farmers, often do not own the land and have to pay rent in terms of labour and a share of their crops. Housing conditions are poor and overcrowded, with no running water and poor sanitation. In the lowlands there are scattered bands of nomadic Indians who are very suspicious of contact with the outside world. Farms are generally too small to support the peasants and their families. There is a long-standing movement of people from countryside to towns and cities, especially Lima. Up to 100 000 people a year arrive there and move into Lima's shanty towns where they live in matting shelters. Lima's population is growing by 7% per annum.

Communications

Communications are poor. Railways run from the coast to mineral rich areas in the uplands and do not form a proper network. Roads are poor, often unmetalled and become impassable in the wet season. Lowland areas rely on rivers for transportation.

In the last 10 years, problems have been caused by Maoist insurgents called Sendero Luminoso (Shining Path) whose aim is to undermine the state and take over the government. A common tactic is to move into a village where they kill the government officials, destroy village halls, TV relay stations and telephone exchanges and ambush buses. Such events are a feature of life in the southern provinces where Sendero Luminoso is strongest. They are now turning on the peasants, in whose name they fight, especially where villages are unprotected. The police and army have retaliated with indiscriminate slaughter to try to wipe out support for Sendero Luminoso. During this period 20 000 people have died and 10 000 'disappeared'. Trouble has spread to the cities with riots and repression in the shanty towns. In the countryside many villages have been destroyed or deserted. Near the northern border with Columbia, the violence and chaos is particularly associated with drug cartels.

The Demographic Transition and Population Pyramids

Population statistics on birth and death rates are often presented as graphs, in particular as the demographic transition model, and as population pyramids. When used together these can provide an excellent picture of the structure of the population and its place in the cycle of development.

Study the graph of demographic transition (figure 2.2).
3 Define the following terms:
   a) birth rate
   b) death rate
   c) natural increase.
4 Describe and explain the differences between the stages shown in the demographic transition. (NB The demographic transition model is based on the Western experience of population change. Sufficient time has not yet elapsed to know whether the Third World will follow this pattern.)
Study the related population pyramids (figure 2.3).
5 Describe and explain the differences between Developed and Third World pyramids.
6 Comment on the problems caused for each country by the structure of its population.
7 How are elements of the demographic transition shown in the population pyramids?

Assignment

A There are considerable differences between fertility (ie birth) and mortality (ie death) rates in the Developing and Developed World. Write a short essay explaining these differences.

Figure 2.2

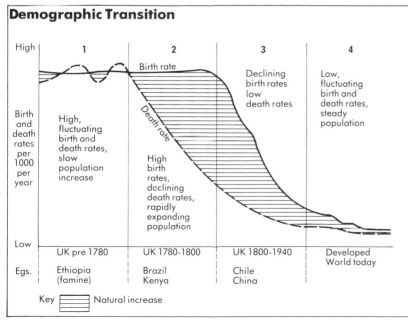

Demographic Transition

Stage 1	High infant mortality, low life expectancy due to disease, famine, poor hygiene, low living standards.
Stage 2	Medical care and sanitation improving, better food supplies, improving living standards, infant mortality falling, life expectancy increasing.
Stage 3	Better health care, high living standards, access to family planning.
Stage 4	High living standards, desire for smaller families, low infant mortality, long life expectancy.

Population pyramids

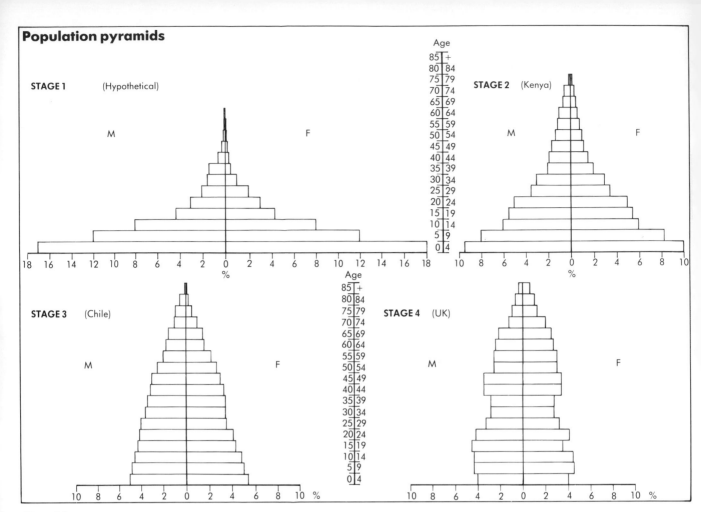

Figure 2.3

SUMMARY

- The census is a valuable planning tool.

- There are many difficulties to be tackled when compiling a census.

- The demographic transition model and population pyramids are interrelated methods of describing the stage and structure of a population.

- The demographic transition model is based on Western experience and may not fit the experiences of the Third World.

- Both the Developed and the Third World have problems due to the structure of their populations.

- Fertility and mortality rates are constantly changing under the impact of modern medicine and technology.

3 MIGRATION

KEY CONCEPTS

Change, Diversity, Interdependence

TYPES OF MIGRATION			
	Voluntary		Involuntary
	Short term	Long term	
Internal	Commuting	Rural/urban	Forced
	Holidays	Urban/urban	Resettlement
	Transhumance		Refugees
	Nomadic herders		
	Agricultural labourers		
International	Holidays	'New life'	Slavery
	Contract workers		Refugees
	Migrant workers		

Table 3a

1 Define the term migration.

Migration takes many forms and has varied over time.

2 Look at table 3a and give an example of each of the types of migration listed.

Reasons for Migration - Push or Pull?

The decision to migrate is not easy. Many factors have to be taken into account before such a decision is made. The further the move and the more permanent its nature, the stronger the reasons have to be.

The following list shows factors which either push someone from their original home or pull them towards a new one.

Availability of work
Few opportunities
Freedom from religious/
  political oppression
High unemployment rates
War/disaster
Opportunities for
  advancement
Low standard of living
Famine and drought

Access to better
  health care
Availability of farm
  land
Access to better
  education
Poor infertile farms
Access to better
  housing
Higher wages

3 Classify these factors into 'push' or 'pull'. You may be able to add others to your list.

Effects of Migration

Look at the population pyramids in figure 3.1. A represents an area of heavy in migration, B an area of out migration.

**4 How does migration affect the population structures of a) the sending
  b) the receiving country?**
You should mention age and sex groups involved.

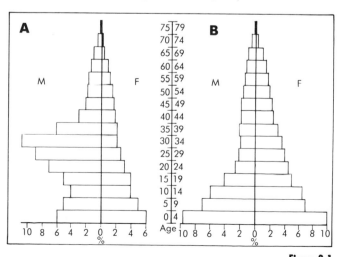

Figure 3.1

15

Countries experiencing high rates of out migration in the Developing World may find that there is a reduction in the pressure for employment and in some cases a fall in the birth rate as those who leave are normally in the productive and reproductive age group. These countries may also receive remittances from their overseas populations which can be of considerable importance to their economies. For example both Sri Lanka and Pakistan until recently have benefited from money earned by their nationals in the Gulf States, such as Kuwait and Saudi Arabia, where there was an acute shortage of labour.

On the other hand these countries are losing the young, fit, best educated and most enterprising members of the society. Those who are left are often less able to improve their lot and that of the country.

The receiving country in the Developed World acquires a source of labour for the low paid, unpleasant jobs which the local population are often unwilling to do. The educated immigrants often fill vital gaps in skilled jobs such as medicine. Large numbers of immigrants, however, put great strains on housing, educational facilities and medical care in the receiving countries.

RURAL/URBAN MIGRATION

Case Study: Nigeria

Any study of Nigerian population characteristics has to take into account the lack of reliable population data. The last official census was conducted in 1963. Since then population data has been arrived at by extrapolation (making estimates or projections) from the 1963 figures. There is considerable evidence that the 1963 figures were themselves highly inaccurate. Such is the uncertainty about the figures that all that can be said about the total population is that it lies somewhere between 80 million and 100 million.

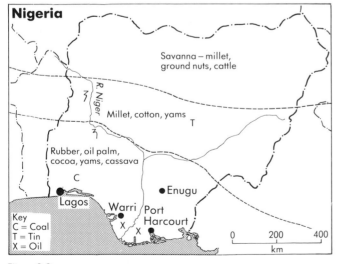

Figure 3.2

Agricultural progress in Nigeria was affected by the oil boom in the 1960s and the civil war of 1967-70. The oil boom generated foreign capital so the country found it could afford to import cheap food-stuffs. This meant that local farm prices fell and farmers had no profits with which to modernize and expand. The result of this was that there was virtually no growth in agricultural output, most farms remained under 3 hectares and the needs of the small farmer were not considered. As a result, farmers found it difficult to make a living in the countryside and many of the younger people began to leave and move into the towns.

At the same time there was an increasing demand for labour in the growing industrial towns such as Warri (iron and steel), Port Harcourt (oil refining) and Enugu (mining). In addition, riverine and coastal centres were growing rapidly as centres of trade and commerce.

Lagos, the chief port of Nigeria, is the fastest growing city in Africa. It is growing so rapidly that it is difficult to gather accurate figures. It is estimated, however, that half the population is under the age of 15 and that 5 per cent of all Nigerians now live in Lagos. Lagos has been called the dirtiest city in Africa. There are severe traffic jams and overcrowded public transport; slum areas which lack piped water, proper sanitation and have no refuse collections; overcrowded housing and high infant mortality rates.

In addition to the prospect of employment, the towns and cities also attracted people because they had schools and universities, hospitals, shops and entertainment to offer. However, in the 1980s the pace of urbanization slowed and in some areas was even reversed. This was due to the catastrophic drop in the income from oil which followed the world slump in oil prices. Not only did Nigeria receive 90% if its export revenue from oil but adherence to the OPEC oil quotas meant that total oil production fell.

Throughout the 1980s Nigeria had contracted considerable international debts and experienced periods of high inflation. All this led to rising unemployment in the cities and a movement of the unemployed back to the countryside and subsistence farming.

INVOLUNTARY MIGRATION

It is estimated that in 1988/89, the world refugee population was 14.5 million people:

    41% were refugees from Afghanistan

    28% were in Africa

    15% were Palestinians.

The rest were from Indonesia, Latin America, SW Asia and Europe.

It is difficult to obtain accurate figures as the refugee population changes rapidly.

Case Study: Refugees in The Horn of Africa

This is a complex area where there have been large movements of people (half the refugee population of Africa). These movements are due to a combination of factors such as famine, independence struggles (Tigrean and Eritrean insurgents in Ethiopia) and civil war (Somali Nationalist Movement and SPLA in Southern Sudan). These have caused massive movements of people between the three countries (Ethiopia, Somalia and Sudan) and their neighbours (Uganda, Kenya, Djibouti). The bulk of the movements are in arid and semi-arid areas, and can result in deforestation, overgrazing, soil erosion and, in the rainy season, impassable road conditions. These refugees are among the poorest and most disadvantaged in an already poor continent, and even if they are skilled or educated, they often end up in unskilled jobs.

However, refugees moving into an underdeveloped area can stimulate its economy. For example in the 1980s large numbers of Ugandans moved into Southern Sudan which was underdeveloped with a low population. The refugees brought in new crops and techniques and supplied labour. Examples like this challenge the common media images and show that refugees are not necessarily helpless and can often do well given the means to help themselves.

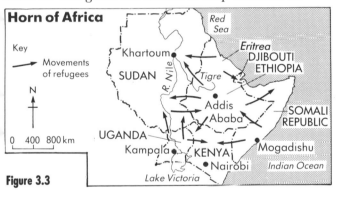

Figure 3.3

SPONTANEOUS INTERNATIONAL MIGRATION

Case Study: Southern Italy

Southern Italy, also known as the Mezziogiorno (the Land of the Sun), has long been an area from which people have left to find a better life. The area is one of poor farming due to its mountainous nature, poor overworked and eroded soils and long summer drought. Too many people try to make a living from the land as there is little or no industrial development. In addition, the area has suffered from natural disasters such as earthquakes and volcanic eruptions which have left people homeless.

Most people are very poor by European standards, live in houses with few amenities (lacking running water and proper sewage services) and have poor education and health care.

In the nineteenth century people migrated to the USA. This avenue closed when the USA introduced quotas which favoured more highly educated and skilled people.

After World War II, people began to leave the south and move to the north of the country or to countries such as Germany where there were shortages of unskilled labour to run the booming industries. In the mid 1970s the area lost 690 000 people (41% to West Germany, 33% to France, 13% to Belgium and 10% to the UK).

Since 1980 there has been a gradual return of the migrants to Southern Italy as the industries of Northern Europe have paid off foreign workers during the world recession. The returnees join the ranks of the unemployed in the south. High rates of unemployment have persisted there, despite attempts by the Italian government to encourage industrial growth. Some of the returnees have made a contribution to the economy of the area, as they have savings which they invest in small businesses such as catering for tourists and in building new homes. They do not, however, have the capital to develop large scale industries.

Assignments

A Using specific examples, describe and explain the effects of migration on both the sending and receiving country.

B Describe the push/pull factors which encourage rural/urban migration. Illustrate your answer with specific examples.

Figure 3.4

SUMMARY

- There are different types of migration.

- Migration is affected by push and pull factors.

- Migration affects the population structure of both the sending and receiving country.

CONTRASTS BETWEEN THE DEVELOPED AND THE THIRD WORLD

Country	Infant mortality	Life expectancy	Population/ doctor	Population/ hospital bed
USA	10	76	470	177
UK	9	75	551	88
India	97	58	2520	1265
Ethiopia	135	47	78970	2787

Table 4a

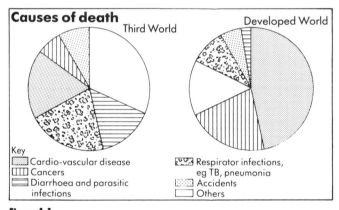

Figure 4.1

Levels of health and health care are good indicators of the level of development in a country.

1 Briefly describe the contrasts between the Developed and the Developing World as shown in table 4a and figure 4.1.

POVERTY

A major cause of poor health and health care levels is poverty. People live in poor quality, overcrowded housing conditions, lacking running water and sanitation. Under these conditions disease spreads rapidly. Poverty leads to malnutrition, especially in children, so that many childhood illnesses are fatal in the Third World.

World health and wealth

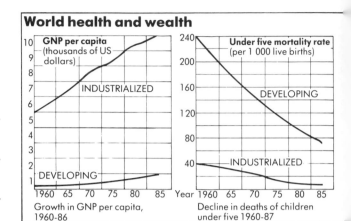

Growth in GNP per capita, 1960-86

Decline in deaths of children under five 1960-87

Figure 4.2

Poor levels of education mean that people are ignorant of the causes of disease, so they are unable to take measures to prevent the continued spread of disease. Improvements in wealth and standards of living make the greatest contribution to improving levels of health. For example, in the UK, rates of infant mortality dropped from 6 per thousand in the 1850s to 1 per thousand in the 1940s (before the introduction of antibiotics and immunization programmes but after improvements in general living standards).

2 Describe and explain how increasing wealth affect people's health.

PHYSICAL FACTORS AFFECTING LEVELS OF HEALTH AND HEALTH CARE

- Climatic conditions have considerable impact on levels of health. Hot, wet conditions encourage the spread of infectious diseases and provide ideal breeding conditions for insects which act as **vectors** (transmitters of disease). Drought and arid conditions affect water supplies, which in turn can result in increased levels of disease as water supplies become restricted and/or contaminated.
- Overused land and poor soils lead to poor farming conditions and low yields which can result in malnutrition. This weakens the population and makes it more susceptible to disease. Children are particularly at risk in these circumstances.
- Mountainous terrain usually leads to poor communications and isolated communities, making the spread of health care and access to medical services difficult.

WATER AND DISEASE

What is dirty, wet and dangerous to health?
The answer is water. Not the water from taps in the Developed World, but water carried by women and children in the Third World, many of whom may have to walk for 3 to 4 hours to fetch it.

Figure 4.3 Collecting water for domestic use in Mexico City

- 57% of people in the Third World (1500 million) lack access to clean drinking water.
- 87% (over 2000 million) lack basic sanitation.
- Poor water supplies cause 80% of all the diseases in the Third World and cause 25 million deaths per year.
- 3000 children die each day from water related diseases.
- Half of the Third World hospital beds are occupied by people suffering from diseases caused by poor water supplies.
- This situation could be improved by access to good water supplies and sanitation.

'The number of taps per 1000 people could be a better indicator of the health of a community than any other.'

3 Explain the above statement.

ACCESS TO CLEAN WATER		
Area	Urban %	Rural %
Americas	93.6	42.5
Europe	91.7	91.7
E Mediterranean	83.9	39.4
Africa	66.5	27.6
SE Asia	70.8	44.3
W Pacific	88.5	28.7

Table 4b

Look at table 4b.
4 Which are worse off, urban or rural areas?
5 In which area is there no difference between provision in urban and rural areas?
6 In the Third World, are most people urban or rural dwellers?
7 Why are urban areas easier to supply with clean water?
8 What would happen very quickly in urban areas if there was no supply of clean water?

In rural areas, if the people are lucky, there will be a well nearby which is deep enough to supply clean water all year round. More likely the well will be too shallow, dry up in the dry season and easily become contaminated by sewage.

Many more people have no water supply close by and may have a long walk to reach a stagnant, polluted pool. In each trip they may carry 15 litres of water. To survive a family needs about 40 litres of water a day. To be able to wash themselves, their clothes and utensils, a family needs 200 litres a day.

Water and the diseases associated with it can be classified as follows:

Water borne - disease is transmitted by people using water contaminated by sewage, eg cholera, typhoid.

Water washed - disease is caused and spreads because people do not have enough water to maintain high levels of personal hygiene, eg leprosy, yaws, trachoma.

Water based - disease is transmitted via parasites living in the water, eg Guinea worm

Water related - disease is transmitted via an insect vector breeding in the water, eg sleeping sickness, river blindness.

Look at figures 4.4, 4.5 and 4.6 and the associated notes on three major diseases in the Third World.
9 Categorize each disease according to the classification above.
10 Which of the diseases is the greatest killer of young children?
11 How can this killer disease be:
    a) treated b) prevented?
12 Two of the diseases may not kill immediately. How do they affect the general health of the sufferer?
13 How does this affect the economic output of a:
    a) farmer b) worker in industry c) student?
14 Why is schistosomiasis (bilharzia) so difficult to treat?
15 A disease such as leprosy can and is cured in the Third World, but those who have had the disease are still regarded as outcasts. Why does this happen?

Case Study: Schistosomiasis

The transmission of schistosomiasis

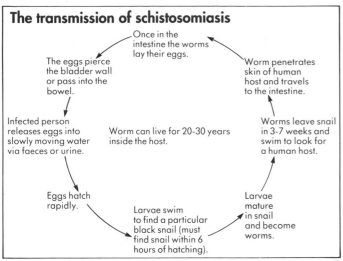

Figure 4.4

Schistosomiasis is a severely debilitating illness which affects 200 million people worldwide, with 10% of sufferers dying annually. In some areas up to half the population can be affected. The incidence of the disease was once almost entirely rural but has begun to spread into the shanty town areas of Third World cities because of their poor water supplies and sanitation.

Treatment is difficult. The snails can be killed by using a molluscide which is highly toxic to other aquatic life. Drug treatment for sufferers is expensive and has severe side effects. The most effective method is to provide adequate sanitation to prevent the larvae entering the water.

Case Study: Malaria

Malaria affects 800 million people worldwide and kills over 1 million infants each year in Africa. Those who survive do have a measure of immunity but suffer from severe anaemia which is severely debilitating and can cause death in adults. Many people suffer from recurrent fever which means they are unable to work. Treatment is complex. Drugs are used on those infected by the disease. Insects are killed by using insecticides and by destroying their breeding grounds. Some of the mosquitoes are becoming resistant to the insecticides used, which can be environmentally dangerous, eg DDT. Drug treatment is also becoming less effective as immunity levels to treatment rise.

The transmission of malaria

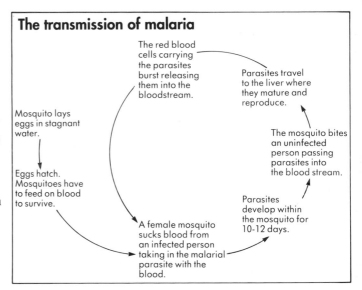

Figure 4.5

Case Study: Diarrhoea

The transmission of diarrhoea

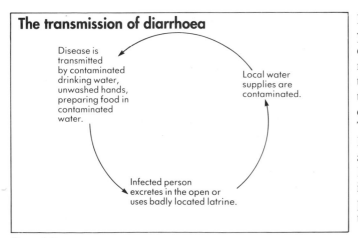

Figure 4.6

Diarrhoea kills 5 million children under five every year due to dehydration and causes 3 out of every 5 deaths of under fives in Bangladesh. Over 100 million people are affected worldwide at any one time but children in the Third World have more than 5 times the incidents of diarrhoea in a year, compared with children in the Developed World. The treatment is simple, cheap and effective - Oral Rehydration Therapy (ORT) which uses a sugar, salt and water mixture to replace lost body fluids. However, permanent alleviation will depend on improved water supplies, better sanitation and a programme of health education to alert mothers to the dangers of using contaminated water.

What can be done?

The years 1981-90 were designated as the UN International Drinking Water Supply and Sanitation Decade. The aim was to provide water and sanitation for everyone by 1990. This was an ambitious target which was not achieved, partly because the cost (an estimated $30 000 million) was not funded completely. Another factor was the continued growth of world population which outstripped efforts to supply clean water and sanitation.

The effort was concentrated on installing water pumps, so that more reliable, unpolluted groundwater supplies could be made accessible. The pumps have to be simple, easy to maintain locally and robust. The second major aim was to install pit latrines which provide a hygienic, waterless way of disposing of sewage in rural areas.

Look at figure 4.9.

16 Describe what has happened to the provision of water supplies and sanitation during the decade.

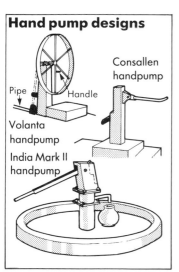

Hand pump designs

Consallen handpump

Pipe
Handle

Volanta handpump

India Mark II handpump

Figure 4.7

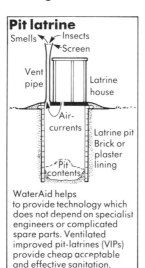

Pit latrine

Smells — Insects
— Screen

Vent pipe

Latrine house

Air-currents

Latrine pit
Brick or plaster lining

Pit contents

WaterAid helps to provide technology which does not depend on specialist engineers or complicated spare parts. Ventilated improved pit-latrines (VIPs) provide cheap acceptable and effective sanitation.

Figure 4.8

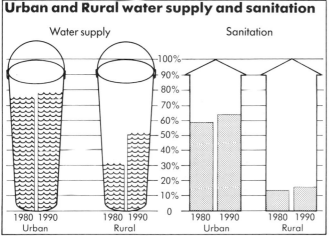

Urban and Rural water supply and sanitation

Water supply | Sanitation

1980 1990 Urban — 1980 1990 Rural — 1980 1990 Urban — 1980 1990 Rural

Figure 4.9

Case Study: Tamil Nadu State,

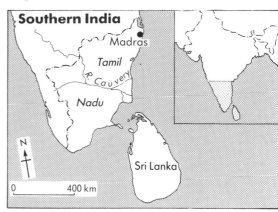

Southern India

Madras

Tamil

R Cauvery

Nadu

Sri Lanka

N

0   400 km

Figure 4.10

Southern India

This is an area with frequent droughts in the summer months when shallow wells, ponds and streams dry up. In the 1970s it was estimated that about 8000 villages in the area had no assured water supply, or at best, only a contaminated supply.

The Tamil Nadu Water and Sewerage Board (TWAD) installed 15 000 shallow well pumps and 15 000 deep well pumps in the 1970s. Responsibility for maintenance was handed over to the village panchayats (elected elders) but maintenance was neglected and at any one time up to 60% of the pumps were out of action. Breakdowns were caused by the wells silting up and by overuse of an insufficiently robust pump design.

TWAD then began to work in collaboration with the UN in the Salem area. Six administrative districts or blocks were involved in a three tier maintenance scheme which, it was hoped, would ensure local enthusiasm and see that repairs were carried out promptly. The three tiers were:

- A village level volunteer or pump caretaker.
- A block level mechanic or fitter for every 100 pumps.
- A mobile repair team at district level for every 1000 pumps.

The caretaker dealt with minor repairs (standard tool kit being two spanners) and informed the fitter if a more serious breakdown occurred.

The project spread gradually throughout Tamil Nadu State and its neighbours. The three tier system was changed and the first tier was taken over by the second tier fitter level, so professionals have taken over from volunteers. Unfortunately the other hoped-for role of the pump caretaker, as a primary health motivator, has not materialized.

Each village has had its own problems to solve, so an all in one package has not been possible. The target now is to supply towns in the area with a clean, reliable water system. This project will be very costly at $150 million, however the World Bank has lent $73 million.

Case Study: WaterAid

Figure 4.11 WaterAid project in Kenya

This voluntary charity was set up in the UK in response to the International Drinking Water and Sanitation Decade by the UK Water Industry. The charity operates exclusively within the Third World for the long term development of clean water supplies and sanitation.

The technology used must be appropriate to the area, as it must be sustainable by the local community after WaterAid moves out. Projects are always undertaken in partnership with a local agency which can be the government or a voluntary body.

The cost per person is generally very low, usually between £2 and £25 per person benefiting from the installation of tube wells, rainwater containers, bore holes, self-help wells and village pit latrines.

WaterAid provides technical guidance and simple construction equipment. The local community provides unskilled labour and accomodation for the visiting technicians.

WaterAid also runs health education programmes along with the projects. Although WaterAid does send in technical experts, it tries to avoid Third World dependency on outside professionals.

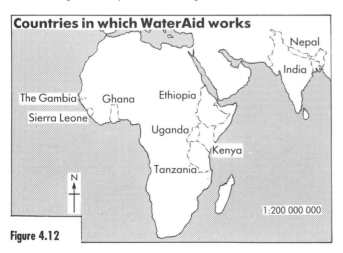

Countries in which WaterAid works

Nepal
India
The Gambia
Ghana
Ethiopia
Sierra Leone
Uganda
Kenya
Tanzania
N
1:200 000 000

Figure 4.12

17 Comment on the two approaches described in these case studies.
18 Which do you think is most effective? Give reasons for your answer.
19 Explain the significance of the logo in figure 4.13.

Figure 4.13 Logo

Improving water supplies and sanitation benefits the health of the whole community especially the women, as they are freed from hours of water carrying and can devote more time to their families. Improved health can also lead to the development of other projects to benefit the community as people have more energy, time and confidence to plan for themselves.

Primary Health Care

The aim of primary health care programmes is to increase the provision of relatively simple health care appropriate to a Third World country. Large, modern, high technology hospitals and highly trained specialist staff are expensive and tend to be concentrated in the capital or large provincial cities, while the majority of the population live in poorly served rural areas.

20 Do you think that such an approach to health care is likely to be effective? Suggest reasons for your answer.

Figure 4.14 Monks giving a health care talk in Bhutan

Case Study: Mozambique

Providing primary health care has been government policy in Mozambique since 1977, when private medicine was banned in order to initiate a free basic service. The policy is to concentrate on sanitation, mother and child health, health education and combating preventable disease.

The government set up a system of rural treatment centres with health workers who had primary education and six months basic medical training to allow them to diagnose and treat simple ailments using 50 medicines. More serious cases would be referred on to regional centres.

Problems encountered:
• Many trained medical personnel left when the country became independent.
• Many rural communities are unable to support a health care worker.
• A crippling civil war has disrupted the whole programme.

Case Study: China

The 'Barefoot Doctor' or medical auxiliary programme was introduced by the Chinese government under the leadership of Mao Tse-Tung in the mid 1960s to improve health provision in the countryside. At that time most villages lacked medical facilities and the nearest, ill-equipped, poorly staffed health centre could be up to 64 kilometres or three days' walk away.

Barefoot doctors were local people, who were given a brief training so that they could attend to their community's needs, from snake bites to appendicitis.

THE STRUCTURE OF THE BAREFOOT DOCTOR SERVICE

Barefoot doctors - clinics for 1000 people, treat minor illnesses, promote health and hygiene.
Mobile health teams - train barefoot doctors during spells when there is less agricultural activity.
Street/community hospitals - treat 25 000 people, a mixture of barefoot and fully trained personnel deal with simple medical and surgical problems.
District hospitals/major teaching hospitals - treat 200 000 people with fully trained medical staff, with full medical and surgical services for the population of an entire region - train doctors and surgeons and offer specialized services

They acted as barefoot doctors for only part of the time, the rest they spent as farm workers. One feature was the combination of western and traditional Chinese methods of treatment. By the early 1970s about 2 million barefoot doctors had been trained (approximately 1 per production team caring for 40 families) and financed as a co-operative medical service into which each family paid a fixed sum.

In the 1980s there were some changes to the Barefoot Doctor Service. For example in Sichuan Province, where many new initatives have been started in the past, there has been the development of small private clinics.

Reasons for changes in the 1980s
• Despite the success of the Barefoot Doctor Medical Auxiliary Service, it has been unable to provide enough health care and health care workers for all, especially in the countryside.
• Some medical auxiliaries lacked skills which led to inappropriate prescribing of drugs and incompetent surgery.
• Some brigades were unable to pay for further training and the co-operative system began to break down.
• The medical auxiliaries suffered from the sheer burden of the work in combining farming and medical work and could often earn more by concentrating on farming and so gave up medical work.

The system set up in the 1970s has not been improved or developed and is therefore collapsing. The hope is that market forces will lead to an improvement in the service which will allow it to cope with the expanding population and the increasing number of elderly in the population.

The government has been encouraging medical auxiliaries, traditional doctors and hospital physicians to set up in private practice. Hospitals have been allowed to charge fees and the government has been trying to encourage private hospitals. The private sector is still only a tiny proportion of China's medical care but could grow in the future.

Figure 4.15 Medical auxiliary in Liaoning Province, North East China

Consequences of changes

There are signs that the decline in rural medical services has stopped but there is no evidence of improved quality. The situation may have in fact worsened for the poor peasants who cannot afford treatment. Real hardships can be caused to the seriously ill, preventative medicine is discouraged and there is less equitable distribution of doctors. This situation makes poor rural areas less attractive than more prosperous urban areas. It also opens the door to swindlers and charlatans peddling dubious remedies. There will probably be a decline in the rational and equitable health service developed in the 1970s, with the poor peasant farmer being the main victim.

21 List the strengths and weaknesses in China's approach to primary health care. How have these caused problems at the present time?

The cost of such a programme in a Third World country is enormous - the cost of the drugs is only 10%, while the remainder is in the cost of setting up the infrastructure. This includes health clinics and centres, mobile health teams, staff, medical equipment and storage of vaccines in a hot climate (solar powered fridges have been developed, and although expensive to purchase they are cheap to run). The drop out rate is a major problem - three out of five patients get the first dose of the diptheria or polio vaccine but only two out of five get the third essential dose. The problem is one of motivation.

24 Why is the immunization campaign so important?
25 Look at table 4c. How effective was the 1989 campaign? Do you think that the WHO achieved its EPI targets by 1990? Suggest reasons for your answer.

The Work of WHO

In 1979, WHO launched a campaign 'Health for All 2000'. This is a global strategy for health for all the world's inhabitants by the year 2000. Health is defined as a state of mental and social well-being. The campaign is not designed to instantly eliminate all diseases. The main purpose is to even-out what health resources there are and provide essential health care for all in an acceptable, affordable way. It is an aim rather than a practical reality, designed to focus attention on the need for action. This will need support from all of WHO's 152 member states, international organisations and the whole world community.

22 What do the initials WHO stand for?
23 What are the aims of the WHO?

Case Study: WHO Immunization Campaign

Six children die and another six become disabled every minute because of inadequate immunization, a crucial preventative measure which costs an average of $3 per child.

In 1974 the WHO launched the Expanded Programme of Immunization (EPI) to immunize against six common forms of disease: polio, measles, TB, whooping cough, tetanus and diptheria. The target date for EPI was 1990, by which time all children were to have access to immunization services.

WHO IMMUNIZATION PROGRAMME (1989)					
	% Children under 15				% Pregnant women
Country	DBCG and	T3	Polio3	Measles	Tetanus
Burkino Faso	67	84	34	68	26
Chad	31	13	13	16	15
Egypt	72	81	81	86	12
Kenya	86	75	75	60	37
Mozambique	47	29	25	39	40
Nigeria	37	21	21	24	17
Uganda	74	39	40	48	13
Argentina	91	75	85	81*	81
Bolivia	31	24	45	33	3
Brazil	68	57	90 a	55	62
Mexico	71	62	97 a	54*	42
Peru	61	43	43	35	4
Saudi Arabia	93	89	89	86	50
India	72	73	64	44	58
Indonesia	74	61	62	55	29
Malaysia	96	72	72	63	25
Austria	90	90	90	60*	n/a
Bulgaria	99	99	100	100*	n/a
Switzerland	90	90	95	60*	n/a
UK	96	70	84	75*	n/a

* Given to children over 1
a Only 2 out of 3 doses
n/a Not available

Table 4c

Case Study: Smallpox Eradication - A Success Story

By the 1950s smallpox had been eradicated in most of the countries of the Developed World. However, 59 countries in the Third World were still affected and the disease was endemic in 33 countries, 25 of which were in Africa. Before the development of vaccination there was no treatment and one person in five died but those who recovered were immune.

A vaccine was developed in the nineteenth century but a technical breakthrough, the development of a freeze-dried vaccine in the 1950s, meant that the vaccine could be used successfully in areas with poorly developed health networks. The vaccine for the eradication campaign was donated by 20 countries. It was found that there was no need to vaccinate the whole population as it was possible to vaccinate selected individuals and contain cases and contacts. This was possible because of the characteristics of the disease. It is transmitted by a respiratory route with no carriers or alternative hosts to act as a resevoir for the disease. Immunity once developed is good. The success rates were so encouraging that the momentum of the campaign was sustained. By 1979 international eradication was certificated.

26 List the reasons why it was possible to eradicate smallpox.

Case Study: Eradication of Malaria - A Failure

The success with smallpox encouraged the WHO to launch a campaign to eradicate malaria worldwide during the 1950s and 1960s. At that time eradication was thought possible using a two-pronged approach, by attacking:
- the mosquito vector in its breeding areas
- the parasites, by using drugs on infected people.

At first death rates fell rapidly. This led to a feeling of complacency. This was coupled with problems caused by large scale movements of people and the growth of breeding areas due to agricultural, industrial and mining developments. The situation was made worse by poor sanitation and lack of health education.

The campaign failed and the WHO have now abandoned the hope of eradicating malaria, admitting that the aim is unrealistic. Eradication has proved impossible because:
- Mosquitoes can survive by feeding on animal blood, creating a reservoir of disease.
- Eradication methods are expensive - draining swamps, spraying pools and houses, and drug treatment.
- Few Third World countries are able to sustain this expense once international aid is withdrawn.
- Eradication is a long term project. If the programme is not sustained and effective it can do more harm than good as people lose their resistance to the disease which they have built up over the years. If the area is reinfected, what would have been a mild fever may well prove fatal. Reinfection can be caused by immigration of infected people. Equally, someone moving from a cleared area to an infected area is a high risk candidate; after Madagascar's eradication campaign failed, 100 000 people died in 1988.
- Resistance to insecticides and drugs increased. By 1979, 30 countries with problems had no control programme and malaria was on the increase in Asia and Central America.

27 Why was the WHO encouraged to plan an eradication campaign against malaria?
28 How did the WHO propose to eliminate malaria?
29 What happened initially?
30 Why did the campaign not succeed?
31 Why is it dangerous to allow malaria to return to an area?
32 What problem arose connected with insecticides and drugs?

India
In 1947 there were 80 million cases of malaria. By 1965, after an intensive eradication campaign, this had fallen to 100 000 cases and total eradication of malaria looked possible. At that point the campaign lost momentum because:
- There was premature complacency about the success of the campaign.
- The Indo/Pakistan War interrupted the spraying programme.
- The closure of the Suez Canal in the Six Day War delayed DDT imports for the spraying campaign and drugs for the treatment of sufferers.
- Mosquitoes were becoming resistant to DDT and parasites to the drugs.
- The spraying campaign was less effective, eg houses were replastered, holy wall paintings left unsprayed.
- Costs rose dramatically during the oil crisis.

Malaria spread once again from its reservoir areas in the subcontinent. Cases of malaria increased rapidly to 6.5 million cases in 1976. Deaths were widespread in a population which had lost its resistance to the disease. The Indian government initiated a new plan to eliminate deaths from malaria and free areas from infection - containment rather than eradication. The infection rate is once again dropping but has not returned to 1965 levels.

The Role of Women

'... The extent to which women are free to make decisions affecting their lives may be the key to the future, not only of the poor countries but of the richer ones too. As mothers; producers or suppliers of food, fuel and water; traders and manufacturers; political and community leaders, women are at the centre of the process of change...'

The State of World Population, 1989, by Dr. Nafis Sadik, Executive Director of UNPF.

The UN Decade of Women was initiated in 1975. The objective was to raise awareness of the role of women who make up half of the world's population, do two-thirds of the world's work, receive one-tenth of the world's income and own less than one-hundredth of the world's property. Women are the major suppliers of family care in the world and one-quarter of all families are headed by women.

33 Apart from child rearing, women fill a multiplicity of roles. List as many as you can.

Women are discriminated against in a variety of ways:
- They are the least well nourished - if food is short girls and women suffer more than boys and men.
- UNICEF estimates that up to half the women in the Third World suffer from anaemia.
- Women are less likely to be educated as shown in table 4d. In the Third World attendance at primary school is as follows; 78% of all boys, 65% of all girls: at secondary school; 48% of all boys, 37% of all girls. The gap is often at its widest in Muslim countries.

PERCENTAGE OF AGE GROUP ENROLLED IN PRIMARY EDUCATION

Country	Male	Female	All
Algeria	99	81	96
Mali	40	17	23
Bolivia	98	85	91
Bangladesh	60	49	59
Indonesia	77	58	67
USA	99	99	99

Table 4d

- Women earn less for doing comparable work. On average a woman's wage is only 40% - 60% of a man's. In addition some forms of employment may not be open to women as they are regarded as male occupations.

- Women have fewer legal rights, eg the right to own property is denied to many women. Women are the major producers of food - they do 60% of all agricultural work in Africa.
- Women have a low status in many countries, which means that their needs are ignored in the development process. Changes often bypass them, eg increased mechanisation of agriculture may positively harm their livelihood by destroying traditional craft industries.

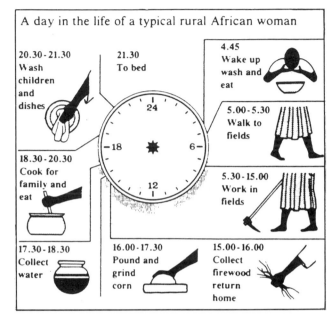

Figure 4.16

34 How does the typical day in figure 4.16 compare with the typical day of a British woman?

35 List the ways in which women in the Third World suffer discrimination. Do any of these apply to women in the Developed World?

WOMEN AND HEALTH

It has been estimated that three-quarters of all illnesses in the Third World could be prevented by better nutrition, a safe water supply, improved sanitation, immunization and basic health care. These are all areas of life where women play a central role in the family.

It has been shown that education of women is a key factor in influencing family health, especially that of young children. For example it has been suggested that for every year of extra education of women in a country, infant mortality drops by 9 per 1000, irrespective of other developments.

Why? This could be summed up in the phrase 'too many, too close, too young, too old'.

Too many - Women who are educated are more likely to have access to, and explore the possibilities of, family planning. They will therefore, tend to have smaller families. For example, in Brazil educated women have on average 2.5 children, uneducated women an average of 6.5 children. Women are more able to spend time with their families if there are fewer children and a woman's health is likely to be better, as repeated pregnancies undermine a woman's health. A mother in poor health is likely to give birth to a baby with poor health.

Too close - Educated women with access to family planning have fewer, more widely spaced pregnancies. As well as allowing the mothers to devote more time and energy to each child, it is much easier to breastfeed each child. These babies generally have a high birth weight - babies with low birth weights are less resistant to infection and are more likely to die in infancy. Breast milk contains natural antibodies which allow babies to fight off some diseases in their first few months. Uneducated women seldom have time to recover fully between pregnancies and are unable to devote their time to the infant. They are often unable to breastfeed their babies and turn to powdered milk. Illiterate mothers cannot read the instructions on the labels of tins of powdered milk, so do not understand the importance of sterilization of equipment. Many also try to 'stretch' the supply of milk by overdiluting it as it is an expensive item for a poor family. Both problems have an adverse affect on infant health.

Too young - Educated women are older when they marry, whereas uneducated women are generally married in their early teens - by the age of 18, 50% of girls in Africa, 40% in Asia and 30% in Latin America are married and have had children. This may be dangerous as the teenagers are often undernourished and underdeveloped physically, especially if they have been malnourished as children. They are five times more likely to suffer complications in childbirth than women in their twenties. Their babies are more likely to be premature and sickly. Their health in adult life is also affected by these early pregnancies.

Too old - by the age of 35, many poorly educated women in the Third World will have had many pregnancies. This, coupled with hard physical labour at home, in the fields and factories, may have destroyed their health. These women often suffer severe complications during childbirth. They are less likely to attend antenatal clinics where 80% of all problems can be identified and they are also less likely than educated women to have a trained birth attendant. As a result they and their children may suffer because of the poor skills and hygiene standards of untrained, traditional midwives.

In addition, educated women are more likely to have their children immunized, have a better understanding of the importance of hygiene and are more likely to take their children to a clinic or pharmacy if they are ill. They are also more confident in demanding health care for themselves.

A mother's nutrition level is also important. Women are often malnourished as children, so that their development is stunted as adults. They are overworked and underfed as adults - between 20% and 45% of women of childbearing age in the Third World do not get the WHO recommended daily basic calorie intake (2500), far less any extra when pregnant. Their children are therefore likely to be sickly, stunted, underweight, prone to disease and have high mortality rates.

Assignments

Figure 4.17 Source: Centre for World Development Education

A Look at the cartoon in figure 4.17. What are the implications for the health of a family in such a situation?

Africa: water supply and sanitation service coverage

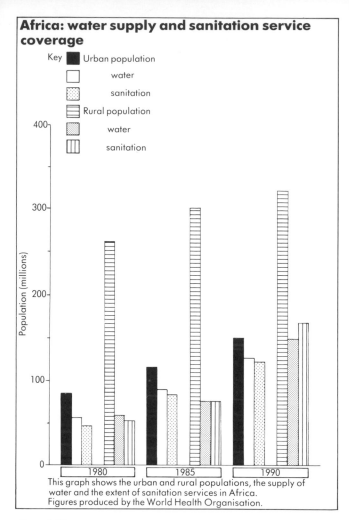

Key
- Urban population
- ☐ water
- ▦ sanitation
- Rural population
- ▦ water
- ⫼ sanitation

Population (millions)

This graph shows the urban and rural populations, the supply of water and the extent of sanitation services in Africa.
Figures produced by the World Health Organisation.

Figure 4.18

B Look at figure 4.18. Describe, with specific examples, international efforts to improve water supplies.
C Describe the original structure of primary health care in China and the changes which are taking place, giving reasons for the changes.

ENCOURAGE EDUCATION

Acute respiratory infections kill between two and three million children a year. But if parents recognize the danger signs they can get help. And knowledge about hygiene helps prevent diseases like tetanus. This can arise from unclean birth conditions and kills around 800,000 new-borns every year. Diarrhea kills around five million infants annually and is spread by germs entering the mouth – often from unwashed hands. Educating mothers can prevent such deaths. Children are less likely

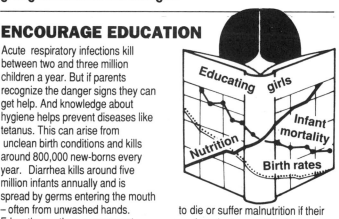

to die or suffer malnutrition if their mothers have completed primary education .

Figure 4.19 Source: New Internationalist,1989

NURTURE MOTHERS

Approximately half a million Third World women die of maternal causes every year leaving behind one million motherless children. In Africa there are almost 700 maternal deaths for every 100,000 live births and in South Asia there are over 500 – compared with 10 in industrialized countries. One quarter of these deaths are the result of inadequate time lapses between babies. Another quarter result from illegal abortions which could have been avoided by the provision of contraceptive services. Around 59% of all pregnant women in Third World countries are anaemic.

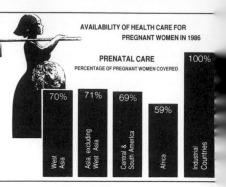

AVAILABILITY OF HEALTH CARE FOR PREGNANT WOMEN IN 1986

PRENATAL CARE
PERCENTAGE OF PREGNANT WOMEN COVERED

- West Asia 70%
- Asia, excluding West Asia 71%
- Central & South America 69%
- Africa 59%
- Industrial Countries 100%

Figure 4.20
Source: New Internationalist,1989

D Describe, with specific examples, the results of the WHO campaign to eradicate malaria.
E Look at figure 4.19 and explain its significance.
F Look at figure 4.20. Describe what it shows and explain why this is so important for a family.

SUMMARY

- There are differences in health levels and causes of disease between Developed World and Third World countries.

- Levels of health are affected by physical and social factors.

- A clean water supply is crucial to good health.

- Many diseases are closely associated with water supply.

- Primary health care is an attempt to provide an equitable, affordable, appropriate health service.

- World eradication of all diseases is an unrealistic goal.

- Women play a crucial role in family health levels.

- Education is an important factor in improving health levels.

PROBLEMS OF DEVELOPMENT

There are many theories to explain the different levels of development throughout the world. No single theory explains these differences fully but each has a contribution to make when trying to reach an understanding of world patterns of development.

The Rostow Model

This theory was developed in the 1960s by a US economist who suggested that countries passed through an identifiable series of development stages as follows:

Stage 1 - Traditional Society - a self sufficient economy, based on hunting/gathering and/or subsistence farming using limited technology and isolated from the outside world.

Stage 2 - Preconditions for Take Off - outside influences allow groups to specialize in the output of primary products as a market develops. Communications improve and small towns develop.

Stage 3 - Take Off - a key stage of 20 to 30 years during which wealth accumulated by trade is invested in the latest technology of the day associated with manufacturing products to produce goods for export. This in turn generated wealth for the next stage.

Stage 4 - Drive to Maturity Industrialization spreads across the economy, new industries develop, large towns and cities grow, eg on coalfields and as ports.

Stage 5 - Age of Mass High Consumption - Wealth spreads throughout the economy leading to mass consumption. Improvements in technology frees labour for a move into an expanding tertiary area. Major conurbations develop.

Stage 6 - Post Industrial (added to Rostow's original model) - growth of economy slows to zero, traditional manufacturing industry in decline, high technology industry main growth area, more leisure.

This model is based on Developed World countries. It was suggested that Third World countries would follow the same pattern of development. This expectation meant that in the 1960s, some Third World countries adopted development programmes which concentrated on large scale industrial

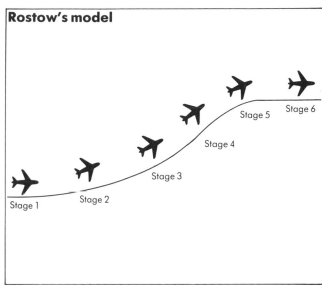

Rostow's model

Stage 1

Stage 2

Stage 3

Stage 4

Stage 5

Stage 6

Figure 5.1

developments in an effort to induce Stage 3 in their development cycle.

Since the 1960s there have been criticisms both of the theory itself and also of the attempt to apply it to Third World countries:

- The model was based on a very small sample - 15 countries in total, which is hardly representative of the variety in the world.
- Many critics believe that the 20 to 30 year take off stage does not in fact exist.
- The Developed World was able to use the resources of the whole world especially through their empires during their development. They now have power and wealth with which it is impossible to compete.
- Third World countries are not free to develop their economies as they wish. Developed World countries interfere by imposing tariffs on Third World imports. In addition they have distorted Third World economies in the past for their own benefit which makes development very difficult in these countries.

Some areas do seem to have followed the model, eg South Korea and Singapore have reached Stage 4, but it is uncertain whether they will achieve Stage 5.

1 Do you think that it is reasonable to apply the Rostow model to the Third World? Give reasons for your answer.

How does Brazil measure up?

Before 1530

There was a traditional society of Amerindians with a subsistence farming/hunting/gathering economy.

1530-1930

In 1530, the Portuguese invaded Brazil which started a period of economic expansion.

Between 1530 and 1650, sugar was grown for export to Europe.

From 1700-1780, gold was discovered and again exported to Europe.

In 1840, Brazil began to export coffee.

In the early twentieth century Brazil was the centre of the rubber boom. The money generated by these exports was used to develop industry. Growth was, however, halted by the world recession in the 1920s and '30s.

1930s-1940s

The Brazilian government intervened in the economy to maintain prices by buying and burning coffee. Attempts were also made to develop the manufacturing sector by using money from exports, eg the Volta Redonda steelworks.

1950s-1960s

Continued state intervention to promote industrialization with the setting up of state companies, eg Petrobras (State Petroleum Company). Multinational companies were encouraged to come to Brazil by low wages and tax concessions. In turn Brazil gained a pool of technical knowledge and modern industrial plant, especially the car industry. This led to the growth of component plants and a high technology sector. Economic growth in the 1950s was as high as 10%, reducing the reliance on primary products for export. The average income was still low, with a wide variation in earnings throughout the country. Inflation rates rose to over 100% and at the same time unemployment rose, poverty increased and there was large scale rural - urban migration. International debt increased until Brazil became the world's largest debtor nation. A series of military dictatorships continued the programme of industrialization while enforcing political stability.

1970s-1980s

Industrialization had not spread throughout the economy and was confined mainly to the South and South East. There were great differences in wealth and earnings. The country's debt burden was so great, that a large proportion of the national income was used to pay off the interest on the loans. This left little investment income for development of the economy. A return to democratic government revealed many social problems which were concealed during the military dictatorships. International debt repayments were renegotiated to ease the burden of repayments. The government planned to encourage growth rates of between 5% and 6% per annum through high technology industries, expansion of the communications network and increasing the output of manufactured goods. High mass consumption was not achieved because the majority of the population had low incomes, poor living standards, poor education, lacked access to medical services and suffered from high unemployment. Multinational companies affected by world recession, cut back production and sacked workers. International concern over the destruction of the rainforests of Amazonia grew as attempts to develop the area increased.

2 To what extent does Brazil compare with the growth model?
3 What methods has Brazil used to try to encourage growth?

Myrdal's Model

Myrdal, a Swedish economist, developed this model to explain how certain areas developed more rapidly than others. It is based on what has been called the **multiplier effect** and can be applied at different scales, eg - locally, to explain the effects of the opening of a new factory - regionally, to describe the consequences of the exploitation of a new resource - and globally, to explain the growth of areas such as Europe at the expense of the Third World. Myrdal's model is based on the concept known as **cumulative causation**. Its explanation for the pattern of development is given below.

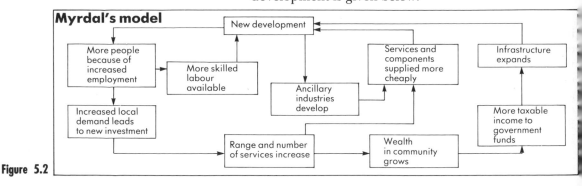

Figure 5.2

Once set in motion new development attracts capital, people and resources from peripheral areas and has a snowball or multiplier effect. These areas are called growth poles where an attractive economic climate is created. This encourages investment, the growth of ancillary industries and the expansion of infrastructure ranging from the communications network to international and satellite industries. Enterprising people move in, the population grows, services expand and new investment opportunities are created. Congestion in the growth area will eventually lead to the spread of development into areas outside the core.

The theory attempts to isolate the elements which cause growth and explain the effects of the **trickle-down theory**, ie that wealth created at a central point will eventually move out to benefit all - the spread effect which may encourage the process of cumulative causation to occur in other regions. The model also helps to explain why the primate cities and/or ports which developed during the colonial period became the centres of development after independence, as these were the most attractive areas to new investment - again the effects of cumulative causation.

Another strength of the model is that it examines the effects of the growth poles on the surrounding areas. These effects are generally negative in character and are called **backwash effects**. The area loses people, usually the most economically active, resources and capital. Local businesses are unable to compete with cheap incoming mass produced goods. The health and education services suffer and are generally poorer than those in the core area. According to the Myrdal model, a country passes through three stages of regional differentiation as it develops:

• Pre industrial - where there are few regional inequalities.
• Cumulative causation and backwash effects causing great regional inequalities.
• Spread effects - reduce regional inequalities. (NB There are suggestions that strong government intervention is also needed to encourage spread effects, as the forces which produce regional inequalities are more powerful than spread effects.)

Many Third World governments have attempted to intervene in the development process by encouraging growth poles in an effort to compete with the richer nations. Some have attempted to open up their peripheral areas by creating new growth poles, eg Brasilia. It was hoped that this new capital city would shift the focus of development in Brazil from the Rio de Janeiro/Sao Paulo axis. This has not proved to be the case. Governmental and administrative functions have relocated to Brasilia but the powerful attractions of the established

centres of industry have proved to be too strong and little industrial development has taken place.

There is little evidence to show that such peripheral growth poles are effective. It is much sounder economically to locate in an area where the infrastructure and raw materials already exist. The model does furnish an explanation for spatial difference in levels of development but does not seem to be a good planning tool, possibly because of the very large number of variables which have to be taken into account.

4 **There are great contrasts in regional development between North and South in the United Kingdom.**
   a) **Use Myrdal's model to explain these differences.**
   b) **How well has the spread effect operated to reduce these inequalities?**

Frank's Theory

Frank, a Latin American political scientist, attempted to explain spatial inequalities in development by using an historical perspective. The theory attempted to explain how the Third World became and remains poor despite world economic growth. The theory has three major concepts:

Metropole - this is a rich industrialised country which dominates and controls the economy and future of a less powerful country.
Satellite - a country whose economy and future are controlled by a metropole.
Dependency - the result of the unequal relationship between the metropole and the satellite in which decisions made by the metropole affect the development plans of the satellite.

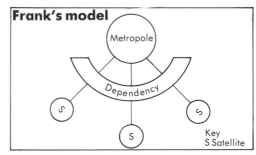

Figure 5.3

This relationship, as illustrated by the model, developed during the colonial era when many European nations controlled the destinies of large areas in the Third World. The economies of these colonies were developed to suit the requirements of the Europeans, eg to produce raw materials for European industry. Local industries were often suppressed. The political and administrative structures of the colonies were also altered to suit the colonisers.

Even after independence the pattern continued as the countries relied on primary exports to the Developed World, their own industrial base was underdeveloped and the cultural heritage of imperialism remained. However, not all former colonies fit this pattern. For example Canada and Australia are both former colonies of Britain.

5   How does Britain's colonial past illustrate Frank's theory?

Blaut's Model

Blaut's explanation of the inequalities of development is based on four significant historical stages or scenes.

Scene 1 - the world in 1492
Europe is traditional and unprogressive with a relatively medieval culture indistinguishable from other similar areas in Africa and Asia. One chance advantage is that Europe is relatively close to the New World which will be plundered and conquered by Europe's superior technology and by the diseases which the Europeans bring with them.

Scene 2 - by 1789
Europe's merchants have used this plunder to surpass their competitors in Africa and Asia and have gained control of European society. They now have the resources to begin the process of industrialisation and through this are able to exploit the resources of the whole world. The non-European world is excluded from this process. Indigenous industries are suppressed, slave labour is introduced on plantations and the non-European world becomes the market for the expanding industries of the continent. These and many other factors favour the increased dominance of Europe arrived at by force.

Scene 3 - 1880
The world is divided into a number of empires funded by a system of exploitation called colonialism. Traditional subsistence farming and indigenous trade has been overthrown and replaced by plantations producing non-food products, large scale forestry operations and mining enterprises which supply the expanding industries of Europe.

Scene 4 - the present time
The colonial empires have gone, but independent nations are still being exploited under a system called neo-colonialism. In it colonial countries have been merged into a single colony called the Third World, exploited by western enterprises. A small proportion of the profits, which come not from fair trade but from forceful exploitation, go to the small elites in the Third World. The exploiters operate through multinational corporations, foreign aid and armament sales.

(Adapted from JM Blaut, The Theory of Development Antipode volume 5 (2) 1973)

6   What are the strengths and weaknesses of Blaut's theory?

7   Look again at the information on Brazil on page 10. Use the information to discuss the relevance of Blaut's theory to development in Third World countries.

The four theories or models of development which have been described all have something to contribute to the debate about the development process throughout the world. The ideas evolved by Frank and Blaut are considered to be radical as they ask us to consider the justice and morality of many of the political and economic relationships in the world today. Rostow and Myrdal are less radical and are more acceptable to those with more monetarist economic policies.

The Debt Crisis

Figure 5.4 Source: Ken Alexander

How has the crisis developed?

8   What is figure 5.4 saying about the world's financial crisis?

In the 1970s the world economy was experiencing a period of prosperity and growth. International trade was flourishing, so that the sale of commodities was generating a high level of income in producer countries (mainly Third World). Interests rates were low and there was a surplus of money in the system, particularly from the oil producing countries, due to the high price of oil at that time. Third World countries were encouraged to borrow heavily, with every expectation of being able to repay the debt without damaging their development.

There are two main types of debt:
  Official debt owed by governments, and enterprises to governments, the International Monetary Fund (IMF) and the World Bank.
  Private debt owed by governments and enterprises to private international banks.

The private banks were very keen to lend to Third World countries as they foresaw good profits from such loans.
There were two main groups of borrowers:
  The poorest countries, including mainly Sub-Saharan Africa, who borrowed in order to start their economic development.
  Middle income countries, such as Mexico and Brazil, who borrowed to further their programme of industrialization.

● **Why was borrowing so easy in the 1970s?**

WHAT WENT WRONG?

Total external debt, selected countries, 1980–87

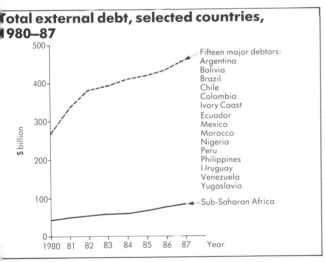

Figure 5.5

10 Use figure 5.5 to describe what happened to world debt in the 1980s.

At the end of the 1970s and the beginning of the 1980s conditions had changed radically. The world economy had gone into recession and the demand for commodities fell and prices for these products tumbled. This meant that producer countries were earning far less. Interest rates worldwide rose sharply, making debts much more expensive by adding millions of dollars to the repayments. Figure 5.6 shows the location of the world's main debtor nations.

By 1987 the total external debt of 109 Third World countries was in excess of $1190 billion. Attention was focussed on 19 highly indebted middle income countries, such as Mexico and Brazil, which were the main debtor nations.

The crisis has, however, spread to the world's poorest countries, especially those in Sub-Saharan Africa. Here the amount of debt owed by each country is small, compared to that of the highly indebted middle income group. Due to the weak economies of these countries the proportion of national income needed to repay the interest on the loans makes it impossible for these countries to develop their economies and to introduce social reforms to benefit their people. For example, in 1987/8 Zambia's external debt was $6400 million, which as a percentage of their export earnings for the same year was 670%. Botswana's economy at the same time was stronger, but even its relatively modest debt of $518 million represented 28% of its export earnings for that year. Indeed, the world's poor are giving a peverse form of aid to the rich nations, as the outflow of money from the poor countries in the form of debt repayment is greater than the inflow of money in terms of aid from the Developed World (see table 5a).

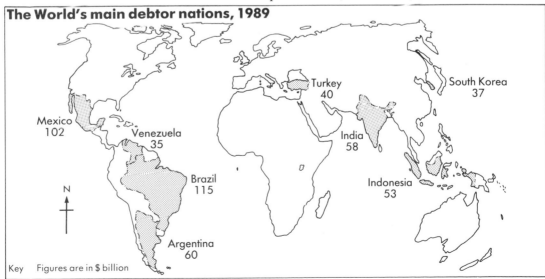

Figure 5.6   Key   Figures are in $ billion

33

The international banking community was badly shaken when, in 1982, debtor countries led by Mexico began to suggest that they would no longer be able to repay the interest on their loans, far less the capital of the loan.

NET CAPITAL TRANSFERS FROM THE THIRD WORLD

Year	$ billion
1984	8
1985	22
1986	31
1987	29

Table 5a

SUGGESTED SOLUTIONS

- Spread the repayments over a longer period. This does not solve the problem but merely delays it because the amount of the debt remains the same. The country concerned still has to find the money to repay both the capital and interest on the loan. The fact that the country has longer to pay, simply postpones its ability to develop its economy and social structures.
- Borrow more to repay the interest. This gets the country even deeper into debt. This solution makes the problem far worse in the long term as debt repayments mount.
- Apply to an international agency such as the IMF to have loans rescheduled. This means having debt repayments altered via guarantees from organisations such as the IMF. This created many internal problems for countries which received help from the IMF. In return for rescheduled and reduced repayments, many debtor countries have to agree to implement very harsh financial policies often affecting education and welfare policies very badly.

11 Briefly explain how the debt crisis occurred.
12 Which groups of countries were affected?

The International Monetary Fund

The IMF was set up in 1947 as part of a proposal to reform the international monetary system. The fund was created by contributions from member governments. The money could then be lent to any member that had a temporary balance of payment problem (ie was spending more on imports than earning in exports). Once the imbalance was corrected the loan could be repaid without any interference with world trade. In the early days, the

IMF helped developed countries which had temporary difficulties, and for this purpose it worked reasonably well. The problem arose when the IMF began to give loans to Third World countries which had more permanent problems.

Once a country had called in the IMF, it had to accept the IMF conditions before the loan was granted. Being refused a loan by the IMF was a serious setback for any country, as it suggested that it was no longer credit worthy! The IMF view was that any country which had got itself into difficulties, had been managing its affairs badly so that they had to introduce austerity measures to correct the situation by reducing consumption. For example, subsidies on foodstuffs had to be discontinued and social services had to be cut back. The idea behind such measures was to encourage the use of local substitutes instead of imported goods and to promote the development of local supplies. This did not work if there were no local substitutes available or if the local economy was unable to supply demand.

Also IMF measures were designed to deal with internal problems. Many of the problems of Third World countries were external and beyond their control, eg the fall in the price of a commodity on the international markets. In practice it meant that countries receiving IMF loans had to cut back on social and environmental programmes.

The poorest members of the community were worst hit, wages fell (for those in full employment), the cost of basic food rose and there were cuts in medical and educational services. The hardship was so great that there were IMF riots in some countries. These were mainly in response to large increases in the price of basic food-stuffs, coupled with high inflation rates which were the results of austerity measures imposed by the IMF in countries in South America and Africa.

The IMF view held until 1985. By this time many debtor nations were facing serious unrest from their populations. At the same time it was obvious to them that the IMF medicine was not working and that their debt position was not improving.

13 How does the IMF work?
14 Why did this cause riots in some countries?

One of the first to rebel was Mexico, in 1982, when interest repayments rose to 50% of export earnings. About the same time, Brazil initiated a $2.5 billion programme of poverty relief and several other countries decided to limit their debt repayments to approximately 10% of export earnings. Peru was one of these countries and when the country missed a payment to the IMF in 1986, Peru was declared ineligible for future loans. Although it is now more difficult for Peruvian companies to get credit, the country's stand does not seem to have caused much damage.

The commercial banks are particularly worried about countries defaulting (not paying what they owe) as many of them have lent more than they have in reserves! Relief agencies have also voiced concern about the effects of the IMF austerity measures on the health and social well-being of people in debtor countries. Even governments in the Developed World have expressed concern about the effects of the massive international debt problem.

WHAT OF THE FUTURE?

In 1988 the principal creditor governments of the highly indebted low income countries met in Toronto. At this meeting, attempts were made to reduce the indebtedness of these countries by rescheduling their debts under the Special Programme for Africa, which gives concessions to those countries which are undertaking significant reforms. This agreement ran out in 1990 and there is no doubt that these countries will need further assistance to reduce their debt burden, which will continue to absorb at least 5% of their GDP during the 1990s.

The recent Brady initiative was aimed at the highly indebted middle income countries whose debt was mainly with commercial banks. Here the effort was to strengthen the economy, encourage private investment and have a partial reduction of debt. Approximately $30 to $35 billion was allocated to help fund debt reduction but much more will be needed in the 1990s to extend the programme. One agency which might well play an important role is the World Bank.

The World Bank

The second of the institutions set up in 1947 to reform international finance was the World Bank. Its main task has been to act as a channel for funds for development projects. It handles $10 billion a year, which makes it one of the largest international development agencies. In the past, 90% of the money has been lent for specific projects identified and approved by the Bank. These tend to be long term projects such as dam building or road construction. Lately the Bank has begun to give loans to countries to help them while they reconstruct their economies. Many think that the Bank should extend its work in this area, although many Bank employees are concerned, as they see this as a move away from the developmental role which the Bank has always undertaken.

The World Bank raises its money on the world's financial markets, which regard it as a safe investment, as its funds are guaranteed by member governments. It is also a preferred creditor, ie it gets

paid before anyone else. The money is then loaned over a long term at a fixed rate of interest.

Not all the Bank's projects have been a success. Some have been economic, social and ecological disasters, as they have a heavy emphasis on developing export industries which will generate a return on the loan.

The Bank does, however, lend to the poorest countries at very low rates of interest. All its loans are at a fixed rate of interest in contrast to those from commercial banks.

The Baker Plan in 1985 wanted to push the Bank into further prominence as it seemed more likely to promote development. Loans would still have had conditions attached to them. The US Congress, however, has not voted the required funds for this initiative (the US is the largest single supplier of funds to the Bank).

Figure 5.7 Source: Wasserman

15 Look at figure 5.7 and explain its message.

The International Debt Crisis has not been solved and it is possible that in the 1990s a country will eventually default. Once one country does so, others will follow. The world's financial institutions would then have to devise a method to cope with these defaults - perhaps by creating a new international organisation to take over the debts from the banks at a discount (ie buying out 80% of the loan and leaving the bank to bear the rest as a loss). Repayments to this new organisation would then be very long term. Many similar schemes have been proposed, most of which involve a mixture of writing off part of the debt and increasing the flow of investment to the Third World.

Case Study: Mexico

- Population 83.7 million
- Growth rate 1.9% per annum
- 23% of the population under the age of 15
- Life expectancy 75
- Infant mortality 46 per 1000 live births
- Daily calorie intake 3132
- Adult literacy 90%
- Average income $1760.

(1988 figures)

The majority of the population is poor but there is a wealthy minority of large land owners and businessmen. The country has a wide range of climatic conditions from desert in the north-west to tropical forest in the south. Much of the country is formed by the central ranges of the Rocky Mountains. The country is also rich in resources (see figure 5.8).

Between 1940 and 1980, Mexico made considerable progress in developing the economy.

16 Describe the trends in employment as shown in figure 5.9.

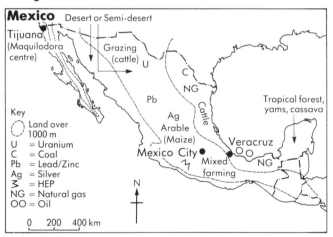

Figure 5.8

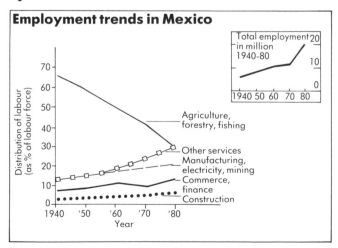

Figure 5.9

During this period, agricultural output increased and more than kept pace with the rising population. Wages also rose during this time and most Mexicans experienced an increased standard of living.

In the mid 1970s, large oil reserves were discovered in the Gulf of Campeche and Mexico became the fourth largest producer of oil in the world. Oil accounted for over 50% of the country's export earnings. Recently natural gas has been discovered in the north-east of the country.

The main growth area for industry is around Maquiladora. Here foreign companies are allowed to assemble products, so taking advantage of the relatively low wages in Mexico. Initially the majority of the firms came from the United States but recently Japanese and South Korean companies have started to move in. As well as employment in these foreign-owned companies, local businessmen have begun to set up component factories to supply the area, creating further employment. The workers here are amongst the best paid in Mexico.

The high oil prices in the mid 1970s, encouraged Mexico to borrow heavily from foreign commercial banks. These banks saw Mexico as a good risk because of the oil revenues and the strides the country was making in developing industry. Between 1976 and 1982, Mexico borrowed $60 billion to finance a variety of development projects.

In the late 1970s and early 1980s, Mexico was hit by falling oil prices and rising interest rates. In addition, Mexico suffered from 'capital flight'. This means that money which could have been invested in Mexico, was taken out of the country and invested abroad where interest rates were higher and the economy stable. Some of the money 'loaned' to Mexico never left the foreign banks. In the 1980s, a newspaper in Mexico City published a list of 575 Mexican citizens who each had $1 million or more invested abroad. It has been calculated that if all this money was invested inside Mexico, the country could repay up to half of its foreign debt. Such a return of capital is, however, unlikely until stable economic conditions are re-established in the country.

In 1982, Mexico shocked the world banking community by announcing that its Central Bank did not have enough in the reserves to meet outstanding debt repayment. The banks then refused to lend Mexico any more money. At that stage the IMF were called in to negotiate a package to reschedule Mexico's debts. The loan was granted but the austerity measures it demanded led to high inflation, low wages and plummeting living standards. In 1985 Mexico rebelled as interest repayments rose to 50% of export earnings. The debt owed by Mexico was equivalent to over $1000 for every poor shanty town dweller around Mexico city. At that point Mexico began to renegotiate the debt burden by using a number of strategies. The terms of $77 billions worth of debt were renegotiated by getting longer to pay off the debt and receiving money to pay off the interest. Mexico also managed to buy back some of its debt at a discount (ie payed 80% of what the debt was worth) in return for long term securities which they would pay in the future.

In 1990, Mexico was the first country to complete negotiations for debt rescheduling under the Brady plan which covered $49 billions of debt and provided $12 million interest relief.

Despite all these measures, Mexico still has a massive debt burden and needs to lower inflation, stabilize the economy and promote investment before progress and further development can take place.

17 To what extent have Mexico's problems been caused by the rich world?

Problems Caused by Development

Third World Development is a growth industry providing jobs for thousands of people, mainly in the Developed World. Despite all their efforts and the considerable sums of money which have been devoted to the development process, the gap between the Developed World and the Third World is as great as ever, if not greater. The phrase 'the rich get richer and the poor get poorer' describes the situation well.

18 Explain why the statement, 'the rich get richer and the poor get poorer', describes the situation of the Third World.

For many in the Third World the development dream has become a nightmare as they see their environment ruined by inappropriate development, their traditional way of life destroyed (often with no compensation for themselves or their families) and poverty increasing as the debt burden increases.

Conventional development does allow a small wealthy elite to emerge in the Third World. The Developed World derives considerable benefits from the development process in having access to low wages and high return on loans in the form of interest repayments.

A number of agencies believe that development has to come from the grassroots and deal with the problems which people face every day. People need to be given a sense of ownership in the development process so that it will be sustained after the 'experts' leave. Local people are usually in a better position to judge what will succeed and the traditional ways of doing things can often be appropriate for the environmental problems known to the locals. For example, in Africa the traditional farmer usually plants a mixture of crops in any one area. This is untidy to the Developed World mind, so agricultural developments producing single cropping systems in neat rows were encouraged. This led to soil erosion, problems with water supply and plant growth, which were not present in the traditional system which had evolved to deal with the environmental difficulties of Africa. The work of the charity WaterAid, referred to in chapter 4, is a good example of small scale grassroots intervention.

19 'Grassroots developments are likely to be more successful than large scale intervention'. Do you agree with this statement and what are its implications for Third World development strategies?

Involving local communities is not an easy task, as they lack organisation and have to be convinced that they can improve their situation.

SOME LARGE SCALE FLOPS

The Polonoroeste Project - Brazil

This started in 1982 as an experiment in land reform. The Brazilian government decided to open up Amazonia and encourage immigration to relieve the pressure of population in the cities and in the south and south-east of the country.

A 1500 kilometre highway was built across the Amazon Basin at a cost of $443 million in loans from the World Bank. Free land along the highway and support services were offered to attract settlers. This has caused massive destruction of the forest, to date an area the size of Great Britain has been destroyed as land was cleared for farming by the settlers. This has endangered the habitat of many animals and plant species and caused severe environmental damage. Native people in the area have also been hard hit by the development as their traditional way of life is destroyed. The land is not fertile and many of the settlers have had to sell up and try to find work in order to survive.

Some people have benefited, eg large landowners have been able to buy up the cleared land cheaply for cattle ranches and there is a plentiful supply of cheap labour to run them. Also some industries have found suitable locations on the cleared land.

OTHER FAILURES

The Mahaveli Irrigation Project in Sri Lanka

Here valuable land has been lost to dams and reservoirs and 1.5 million people have had to be resettled, with little compensation. Rare habitats have been threatened.

Gezira Project Sudan

This ambitious project was designed to promote the growth of cotton as a cash crop for export in the fertile Gezira area of the Sudan. Efforts to boost output to compensate for the rising prices of imports have led to problems. In this area there has been considerable pollution of the environment by herbicides and pesticides used in an effort to increase the output of cotton.

Case Study: The Volta Dam

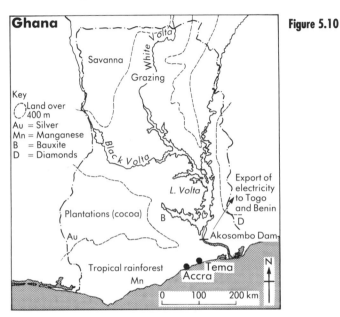

Figure 5.10

This was built in the 1960s with loans from the USA and the World Bank. The project created one of the world's largest artificial lakes, flooding 9600 square kilometres and displacing 85 000 people. The intention was to provide a cheap source of electricity which could be used to process local bauxite into alumina and aluminium sheet for export. It was expected to provide a basis for industrialization to generate exports and lessen Ghana's dependence on primary products, eg cocoa. It was also meant to provide a domestic electricity supply for Ghana and a reliable supply of irrigation water.

What has happened

The extent of the lake has interrupted east/west communications in Ghana and reduced accessibility, especially in the east. Sediment which would have been carried by the river is trapped in the reservoir upsetting the coastal ecology. The people who had to be resettled were not provided with housing suitable to their traditional lifestyle and many were unhappy at the siting of their new homes. Compensation has not been considered adequate. An American company, the Kaiser Corporation, built a smelting plant at Tema and negotiated terms with the Ghanaian government which included a 30 year guaranteed tax rate, 30 years import duty exemption and 50 years cut-price electricity. The smelter absorbs 70% of the electricity produced and only 5% of Ghanaians have electricity from the dam, for which they pay a high price. Some electricity is also exported to Benin and Toga, Ghana's neighbours. All these countries suffer from severe power shortages.

Ghana's bauxite is not being processed at the plant but is still being exported to Europe and Japan where wealth-creating manufactured goods are produced. The bauxite used in Tema is imported from Jamaica with no import duty and uses the cheap electricity, thus allowing large profits to be made by a foreign multinational.

Irrigation schemes have not developed as expected. One of the few benefits has been the creation of a fishing industry on the lake employing 10 000 people. The area has suffered from severe drought, to such an extent that in 1983 power supplies were interrupted and the smelter had to be closed temporarily.

The Ghanain government is currently renegotiating the terms of the 1961 agreement and the aluminium company has agreed to pay increased prices for its electricity.

'...SO YOU SEE, THE ENTIRE FUTURE OF THE INTERNATIONAL FINANCIAL SYSTEM HINGES ON YOUR CAPACITY FOR QUICK RECOVERY AND VAST ECONOMIC GROWTH.'

Figure 5.11 Source: Oliphant

Assignments

A Describe some of the problems of development.
B Discuss the different approaches to development illustrated in the four theories described in this chapter.
C To what extent did the belief in the Rostow model of development cause problems for the Third World in the 1970s and 1980s?
D The amount of debt owed by a country is not always a good indication of the burden which this debt causes. Use table 5b to discuss and explain this statement.
E Study figure 5.11. Discuss the implications for the Developed and Third World of its message.

THE DEBT PROBLEM IN SELECTED COUNTRIES 1989			
Country	Total debt $ billions	Debt serviced (% of exports of goods and services)	Official development assistance $ per capita and (in $ millions)
Middle Income Latin American Countries			
Brazil	114.5	42.0	1.5 (210)
Mexico	101.5	43.5	2.1 (173)
Argentina	59.8	36.0	4.8 (152)
Venezuela	34.6	39.7	0.9 (18)
Chile	19.6	19.1	3.4 (44)
Columbia	17.0	42.3	1.9 (61)
Equador	10.8	21.4	13.6 (137)
Bolivia	5.4	32.9	56.7 (392)
Lower Income Sub-Saharan Countries			
Nigeria	30.7	25.7	1.1 (120)
Ivory Coast	14.0	31.9	39.1 (439)
Kenya	5.8	25.3	36.0 (808)
Cameroon	4.2	27.0	25.4 (284)
Madagascar	3.6	39.0	28.0 (305)
Ghana	3.0	20.6	33.9 (474)
Ethiopia	2.9	37.4	20.5 (970)
Zimbabwe	2.6	27.9	29.3 (273)
Niger	1.7	32.6	51.1 (371)
Other Selected Countries			
India (LIC)	57.5	24.9	2.6 (2098)
Indonesia (LIC)	52.6	39.6	9.3 (1632)
Turkey (MIC)	39.5	35.2	5.7 (307)
South Korea (MIC)	37.1	9.1	0.2 (10)
Yemen PDR (LIC)	2.0	39.6	32.3 (76)

Table 5b

SUMMARY

- Care must be taken when applying growth models to Third World countries

- The international debt crisis has serious implications for both the Developed and the Third World.

- Development does not always bring positive benefits to Third World countries.

GLOSSARY

Development Indicators - Statistics used to illustrate the level of development within a country. They can be divided into economic indicators of development, eg GDP and social indicators of development, eg life expectancy, infant mortality. Composite Indicators of Development employ a variety of indicators.

GDP - Gross Domestic Product - The total value of all goods and services produced within a country (this is an average figure for the country).

GDP per capita - The GDP divided by the total population (an average figure per head of population).

High Income Country - Average income over $6000 per capita in 1988. (World Bank classification)

Low Income Country - Average income less than $545 per capital in 1988. (World Bank classification)

Middle Income Country - Average income $546 to $5990 per capita in 1988. (World Bank classification)

LDC - Least Developed Country - A country identified by UNCTAD as having severe long term constraints on development.

PQLI Index - Physical Quality of Life Index. A method of combining three key indicators of development; life expectancy, infant mortality and percentage of adult literacy to give an overall figure lying between 0 and 100, indicating the quality of life within a country.

Vector - An insect or other carrier which plays a role in the transmission of disease.

SELECTED BIBLIOGRAPHY

A Health and Nutrition Atlas World Health Magazine WHO 0 11 951285 8.

Alternative Approaches to Development Geography 16 - 19 Longman 0 582 17228 4.

Aspects of Social Geography J Geddes, K Muir Edward Arnold 0 7131 7614 8.

Dialogue for Development SCAIF.

Earth Watch People Magazine IPPF.

For Richer for Poorer J Clark Oxfam 0 85598 077 X.

Geofile Mary Glasgow Publications 02677563.

Geographical, Digest 1990-91 Heinemann 0 435 34957 0.

Health in Developing Countries Hobsons Publishing 1 85324 079 6.

Human and Economic Geography G C Leong, G C Morgan OUP 0 19 582816 X.

Meeting the Population Challenge UNPFA 089 714068 0.

People and Environments Ed. F Slater Collins 0 00 327402 0.

Rich World Poor World Macdonald 0 356 10142 8.

Studies in World Development J Farms, F Smith Edward Arnold 0 7131 7449 8.

The Changing Geography of Africa A T Grove OUP 0 19 913319 0.

The Development Data Book World Bank/Longman 0 582 04579 7.

The New Internationalist ISSN 0 305 9529.

The State of the World Population 1988 UNPFA.

The Third World; Development and Interdependence R Beddis OUP 0 19 913329 8.

The Water of Life SCAIF.

The World D Waugh Nelson 0 17 434210 1.

The World Bank Atlas 1990 World Bank 0 8213 1649 4.

Thin Black Lines C Regan, S Sinclair, M Turner Development Education Centre 0 948838 02 7

Third World Atlas Crow Open University Press 0 335 10259 X

Whose Development? Development Education Centre 0 950 66197 X

World Development Report 1990 World Bank/OUP 0 19 5208501

USEFUL ADDRESSES

Action Aid Hamlyn House, Archway, London N19 5PG.

CAFOD The Catholic Fund For Overseas Development 2 Garden Close, Stockwell Rd, London SW9 9TY.

Commonwealth Institute Kensington High St, London W8 6NQ. 8 Rutland Sq, Edinburgh EH1 2AS.

CWDE Centre for World Development Education 1 Catton Street, London WC1R 4AB.

Christian Aid PO Box No 1, London SW9 8BH.

Development Education Centre Selly Oak Colleges, Bristol Rd, Birmingham B29 6LE.

IMF International Monetary Fund.

International Institute for Environment and Development - Earthscan 3 Endleigh St, London WC1H ODS.

International Planned Parenthood Federation PO Box 759, Inner Circle, Regent's Park, London NW1 4LQ.

OECD Organisation for Economic Co-operation and Development.

Oxfam 274 Banbury Rd, Oxford OX2 7DZ.

Save The Children Mary Datchelor House, Grove Lane, Camberwell, London SE5 8RD.

SCAIF Scottish Catholic International Aid Fund, 43 Greenhill Rd, Rutherglen, Glasgow G73 2SW.

Tear Fund 100 Church Road, Teddington, Middlesex TW11 8QE.

United Nations Publications:
  FAO Food and Agricultural Organisation
  UNCTAD United Nations Conference on Trade and Development
  UNFPA United Nations Population Fund
  UNHCR United Nations High Commission for Refugees
  UNICEF United Nations International Children's Emergency Fund
  WHO World Health Organisation.

Scottish Educational Trust for United Nations and International Affairs Conference Room, Stirling's Library, Queen Street, Glasgow G1 3AZ.

United Nations Association of Great Britain and Northern Ireland 3 Whitehall Court, London SW1.

WaterAid 1 Queen Anne's Gate, London SW1H 9BT.

World Bank New Zealand House, Haymarket, London SW1 Y4TE.

The photos in unit 1 are:
Figure 1.1 Toronto, Canada; Figure 1.2 Banaue, The Philippines; Figure 1.3 United Kingdom; Figure 1.4 Favela Rocinha, Rio de Janeiro; Figure 1.5 New York. The cover photo shows Sao Paulo, Brazil.